MATHS DIRE...
Book A

Jean Cheshire
Christine Collins
Mark Pepper
Anne White

Series Editor: **Mundher Adhami**

Collins Educational
An imprint of HarperCollinsPublishers

Contents

Published by Collins Educational
An imprint of HarperCollinsPublishers Ltd
77-85 Fulham Palace Road
London W6 8JB

The HarperCollins website address is www.**fire**and**water**.com

First published 1999

ISBN 0 00 322490 2

British Library Cataloguing in Publication Data
A catalogue record for this book is available from the British Library.

Edited by Dodi Beardshaw

Design by Chi Leung

Commissioning Editor: Alison Walters

Illustrations by Barking Dog Art, Russell Birkett, Jerry Fowler,
Bethan Matthews and Harry Venning

Production by Anna Pauletti

Printed and bound by Scotprint, Musselburgh.

Module A1

Number and measurement

❶ Ordering numbers
Reading and writing numbers up to 100 in figures.
Putting numbers in order

❷ Ordering up and down
Deciding which numbers are bigger or smaller than
other numbers. Counting forwards and backwards correctly

❸ All the coins
Choosing coins to make up different totals of money

❹ Half and half
Finding half-way marks, or whether one part of
something is bigger than another, just by looking

❺ Straight adding
Practising adding tens numbers to a units number
without pen and paper, to solve a problem

❻ Number skills
Practising different number skills

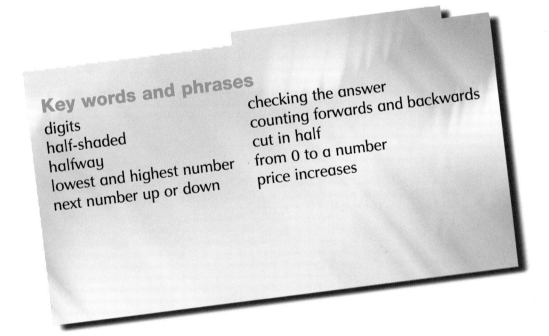

Key words and phrases
digits
half-shaded
halfway
lowest and highest number
next number up or down
checking the answer
counting forwards and backwards
cut in half
from 0 to a number
price increases

❶ Ordering numbers

How easily can you read these?

Look at the picture and answer the following questions.
1. What is the cheapest thing advertised in the picture?
2. What is the most expensive thing?
3. What things are priced nearly the same but not exactly the same?

Write these numbers using digits. Then write them in order starting with the lowest number.
1. fifteen
2. twenty-two
3. sixty-one
4. twenty-eight
5. eighteen
6. seventy-five

Look at the price list on the ice-cream van.

1. Which ice-cream is the dearest?
2. Which ice-cream is the cheapest?
3. List the other four ice-creams in order of their prices.

Paul and his friends have recently had a maths test. Here are their results.

1. Who came top?
2. Who came bottom?
3. Who came second?
4. Who came third?

Maths Test Results/%	
Vicky	58
Hanif	82
Paul	52
Fatima	79
Jason	80
Janet	48

Look at the bookshelf.
1. How many books are there?
2. How many paperback books are there?
3. How many hardback books are there?

The thermometers show the warmest temperature for each day from Monday to Thursday.

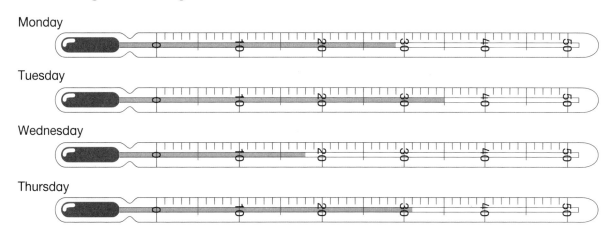

Monday

Tuesday

Wednesday

Thursday

1. Which day is the hottest?
2. Which day is the coldest?
3. Which day is the second hottest?

Now look back at your work in this lesson.
- Think of any new words you have learnt.
- Ask yourself if you are now confident in reading and writing numbers up to 100, and putting them in the right order.

② Ordering up and down

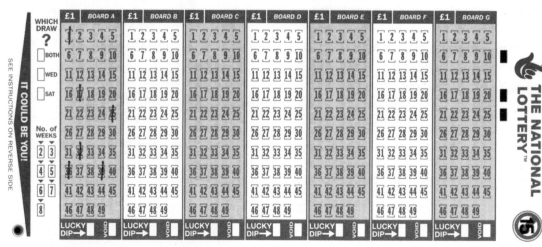

What are the numbers that have been crossed out?
Did you count forwards or backwards to work out the answer?

Copy these numbers and fill in the ones that are missing.

1 15 ☆ 17 18 19 ☆ 21 ☆ 23
2 34 35 36 ☆ 38 39 ☆ ☆ 42
3 42 ☆ 44 ☆ 46 47 ☆ ☆ 50
4 55 56 ☆ 58 ☆ ☆ 61 62
5 10 9 ☆ 7 6 ☆ 4
6 27 26 ☆ 24 23 ☆ 21

Five friends have tickets for a pop concert. They have seats together in Row G. Manday's seat is G37 and Anne's seat is G41. The other three friends have seats in-between.

1 What are the numbers of their tickets?

Imran, Sue, Joanne, John and Errol become members of their favourite football club. Imran joins first and his membership number is 256.

1 Sue joins just after Imran. What is her membership number?
2 Joanne is next. What is her number?
3 John is next. What is his number?
4 Errol is next. What is his number?

John, Simon and Debbie live in a block of flats. John lives at flat 32. Simon has left his door open.

1 What are the door numbers of Simon's flat and Debbie's flat?
2 Which flat is located between John's flat and Simon's flat?
3 What is the flat number to the right of Debbie's flat, and the one after that?
4 What is the flat number before John's flat?

It costs £1 for five raffle tickets.
1 Wasim's book of five tickets starts at 37. Copy and fill in the rest of his numbers.

37 ☆ ☆ ☆ ☆

2 Linda's block of five tickets finishes at 68. Copy and fill in the rest of her numbers.

☆ ☆ ☆ ☆ 68

Sarah is saving her money. She decides to put £1 into her account every week. She has £57 in her account already.
1 How much will she have after one week?
2 How much will she have after two weeks?
3 A few months later she found out that she has £75 in her account. How much did she have one week before?
4 How much did she have two weeks before?

Now look back at your work in this lesson.
• Can you tell which numbers are bigger or smaller?
• Can you count up and down without difficulty?

❸ All the coins

Sometimes only one coin can buy a
lot more than several coins.

 Look at the picture and answer these questions.

1 If you are allowed two coins only what would be the most
money you could have?

2 What is the least you can have with two coins?

 How much is there altogether?

1  **4**

2 **5**

3 **6**

 Tina needs to buy a stamp for 19p. She has these coins in her purse.

1 Which coins does she need?

2 How much more does she need to buy another 19p stamp?

Aiden is collecting money from his family for charity. He gets these amounts.

 Mum Dad   big brother

 sister baby brother

1 How much did Aiden collect altogether from his family?

2 Is it true that he collected from Mum more than all the others put together?

3 How much does he need to make £1?

Wendy is selling the class magazine.
On the first day, she sells three copies and receives these coins from her friends.

Hanif   Vicky

Helen

1 What is the price of the magazine?

On the second day, she sells two copies and receives these coins from her friends.

Peter   Jamelia

2 How much did she get altogether on the second day?

On the third day, she sells four copies and receives these coins from her friends.

Abbas   Debbie

Paul's Mum   Fatima's Gran

3 How much did she sell altogether on the third day?

4 How many magazines did Wendy sell over the three days?

5 How much money did she collect altogether?

6 How can you check your answer?

The sweet shop sells drinks and sweets.

1 Wasim has

How much does he need to buy a fun-size bar?

2 Can he buy a fun-size bar and another sweet?

3 Helen has

Can she buy a cola drink?

4 What can she buy?

5 Paul has

Can he buy some bubble gum?

6 Can he buy any other sweet?

7 Najma has

Can she buy some crisps?

8 How much will she have left?

Now look back at your work in this lesson.
- Do you know what all the coins look like?
- Can you choose coins to make up any amount of money?

④ Half and half

Which plate would you choose?
Why?

For each group of three
shapes, write down which shape
is half shaded – **a**, **b** or **c**.

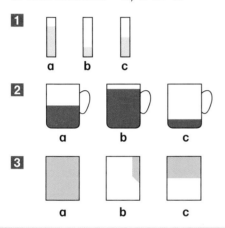

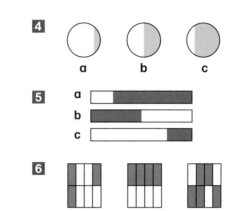

Here is some fruit cut in half.
How many whole fruits will these pieces make?

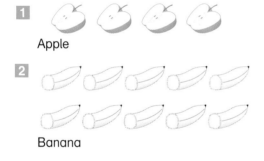

1 Apple

2 Banana

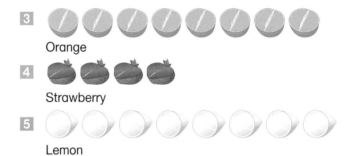

3 Orange

4 Strawberry

5 Lemon

Ming and Debbie buy these groceries. They share them so
that they both have half of them. How many of each item do
they both have?

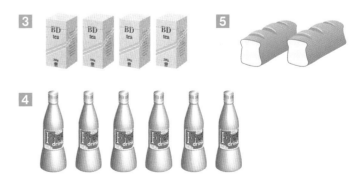

Abdul and Hussain are brothers. Their mum gives them some money to share equally.

1 How much does Abdul get altogether?
2 How much does Hussain get altogether?

At John's sports club, each game of basketball lasts 1/2 hour.
How many 1/2 hour games can be played in these times?

1 1 hour
2 6 hours
3 5 hours

4 4 hours
5 1 1/2 hours
6 2 1/2 hours

Use the picture of the ruler to answer the questions by finding exactly half-way to the number. Here is an example to help you.

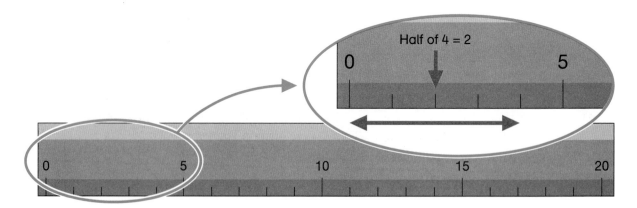

Half of 4 = 2

1 What is half of 6?
2 What is half of 10?
3 What is half of 2?
4 What is half of 20?

5 What is half of 8?
6 What is half of 4?
7 What is half of 16?
8 What is half of 18?

Now look back at your work in this lesson.
- Can you tell just by looking if something is over or under half full?
- Can you tell just by looking if something is bigger or smaller than something else?

⑤ Straight adding

How do you work out the answer to such a sum?

A Work out the answers to these sums in your head and then write them down.

1. 20 + 7 =
2. 40 + 6 =
3. 6 + 70 =
4. 6 + 30 + 20 =
5. 80 + 10 + 8 =
6. 10 + 10 + 6 =

B Here are the ages of everyone in Fatima's family.

1. Fatima is 10 years old. How old will she be in 5 years' time?
2. Her sister is 20 years old. How old will she be in 3 years' time?
3. Her dad is 40 years old. How old will he be in 7 years' time?
4. Her mum is 40 years old. How old will she be in 6 years' time?
5. Her grandad is 70 years old. How old will he be in 8 years' time?

C Peter and his friends are saving money to buy computer games.

1. Peter has £20 in his account. He saves £6 more.
   How much does he have now?
2. Hussain has £10 in his account. He saves £8 more.
   How much does he have now?
3. Anna has £30 in her account. She saves £1 more.
   How much does she have now?
4. Roger has £50 in his account. He saves £7 more.
   How much does he have now?
5. Fatima has £60 in her account. He saves £3 more.
   How much does he have now?

D Debbie's local sweet shop has price increases of 2p on all items.
What are the new prices?

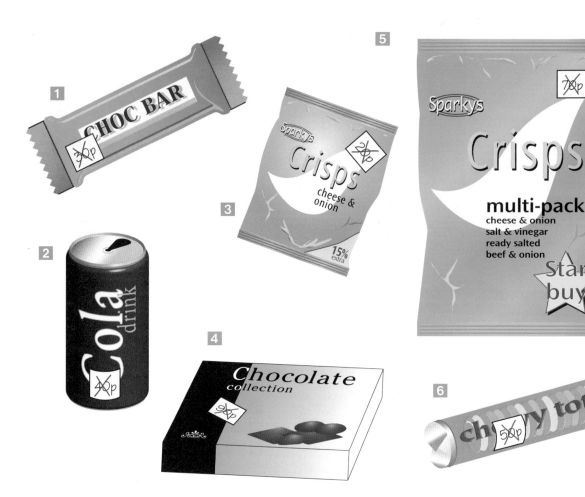

E Lee's class is given English homework. Each student has to read
ten more pages of the book they have started. Which page must
each of them reach?

1 Lee has read six pages. Which page must he reach?

2 Fiona has read four pages. Which page must she reach?

3 Abbas has read eight pages. Which page must he reach?

4 Hasim has read three pages. Which page must he reach?

5 Rushna has read nine pages. Which page must he reach?

Now look back at your work in this lesson.
- Practise adding up tens with units in your head.
- Think about how you do different sums in your head.

⑥ Number skills

In a very long queue sometimes you can take a ticket to show which is your place.

At the delicatessen counter Errol has taken ticket number 41 and is waiting for his turn. It is number 36's turn.

1 What are all the numbers that the machine will show before Errol's turn?

2 If each turn takes about one minute, how long will Errol wait before his turn?

Copy and fill in the missing numbers.

1 41 42 43 44 ✳ ✳ ✳ ✳

2 ✳ ✳ ✳ ✳ 37 38 39 40

3 71 ✳ 73 ✳ 75 ✳ 77

4 ✳ ✳ ✳ 54 55 56 ✳ ✳ ✳

5 29 28 27 ✳ 25 ✳ ✳ ✳

Calculate these answers.

Orange drink **37p**

Chocolate bar **62p**

Football cards **45p**

High-bounce ball **22p**

1 Mohammed wants to buy an orange drink. Which coins will he need?

2 Janet wants to buy a bar of chocolate. Which coins will she need?

3 Which coins are needed to buy the set of football cards?

4 Which coins are needed to buy the high-bounce ball?

5 Choose two things from the list. Which coins would you need to buy them both?

Use tracing paper to copy these pictures. Draw in the other half.

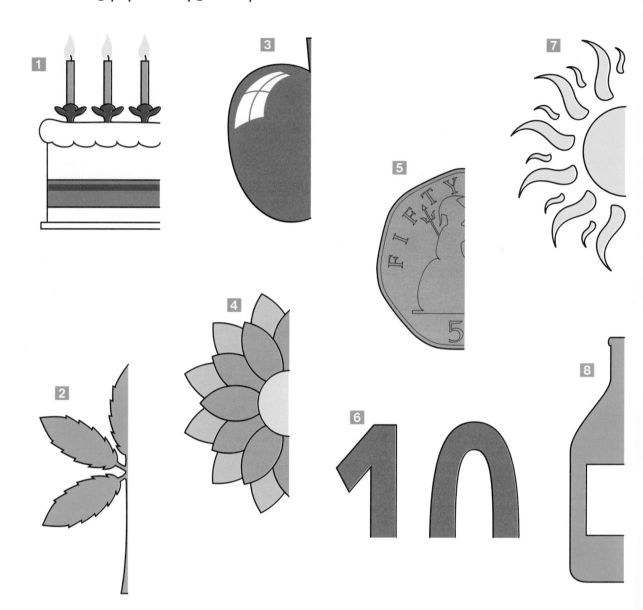

Write the answers to these sums without any written working out.
1 30 + 6 =
2 80 + 8 =
3 90 + 7 =
4 10 + 40 + 5 =
5 20 + 10 + 4 =
6 70 + 6 =

Now look back at your work in this lesson.
• Think about all the different number skills you have learnt.
• Think of any new words you have learnt.

18

Module A2

Handling data

1 **From pictures to bar charts**
Considering different ways of showing how many there are

2 **Ordering**
Putting things in order, by size, by number, by strength
of colour, or by other rules

3 **Order and bar charts**
Ordering skills together with reading of bar charts

4 **Doubling and halving**
Practising halving and doubling together with bar charts
and picture patterns

5 **Comparing charts**
Looking at two charts and finding more information
from comparing them

6 **Bar chart skills**
Drawing bits of bar charts when you know the numbers
and the scale

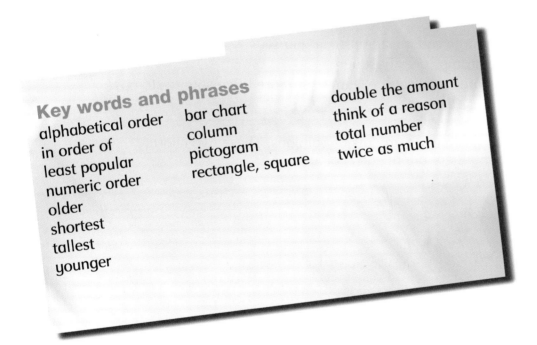

Key words and phrases

alphabetical order
in order of
least popular
numeric order
older
shortest
tallest
younger

bar chart
column
pictogram
rectangle, square

double the amount
think of a reason
total number
twice as much

① From pictures to bar charts

A few large signs can take more space than many small signs. You must not confuse the number of things with how big or small they are.

Look at the stamps.

1 How many large square stamps can you see?
2 How many stamps are not square?
3 Are there more small square stamps or more large square stamps?

At a children's party there are lots of balloons. These two charts show how many there are of each colour.

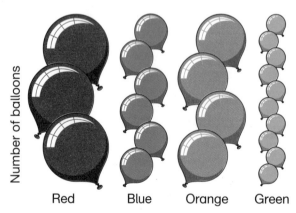

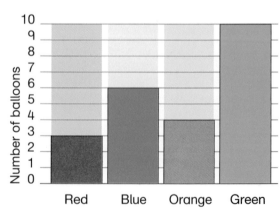

1 How many red balloons are there?
2 Are there more green balloons or blue balloons?
3 Do both of the charts show the same number of each colour?
4 Which one do you think is the clearest and easiest to use? Can you explain why?

C In the school car park there are seven blue cars, five green cars, four red cars, six white cars, ten yellow cars and four black cars.

1. John and Winston drew a bar chart to show this but they made two mistakes. Can you find the mistakes that they made?
2. Is it true that there are more yellow cars than blue cars?
3. Is it true there are fewer black cars than red cars?

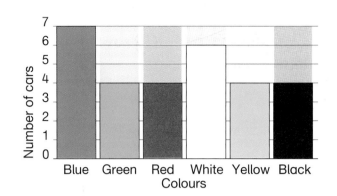

D Rakhee asked her class to choose their favourite pet. They drew a picture graph to show the results.

1. How many of her friends chose a dog?
2. Which was the least popular pet?
3. Were there more rabbits or more birds chosen?

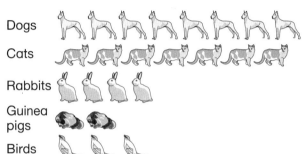

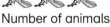

E John, who prefers not to draw pictures, drew columns to show Rakhee's results. Winston wanted his to look different so he drew rows. Use the boys' charts to answer the questions.

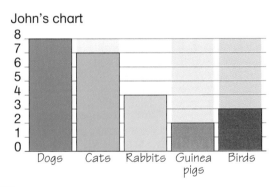

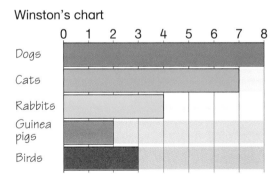

1. How many pupils chose a cat as their favourite pet?
2. Which pet was twice as popular as the rabbit?
3. How many pupils were in the class?
4. Whose chart do you think shows the results in the best way – Rakhee's, John's or Winston's? Why?

Now look back at your work in this lesson.
- Do you understand the difference between a pictogram and a bar chart?
- Which do you think is the best way to show a number of things?

② Ordering

The farmer prepares food separately for each animal.

A

Look at the picture.
1 Which feeding bowl belongs to which animal?
2 How did you decide that?

B

Give the answers to these questions about order.
1 What should the order of numbers for the houses be?

2 Arrange these numbers in order starting with the smallest.
17   9   15   11   7   5   13

C

Here is a row of rectangles.
1 Which rectangle is the tallest?
2 Which one is the shortest?
3 Is rectangle **e** taller or shorter than rectangle **a**?
4 Put the rectangles in order starting with the shortest.

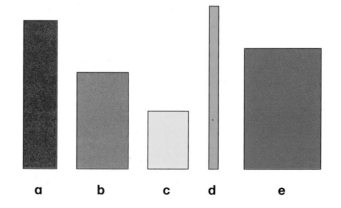

a   b   c   d   e

A car is available in five different colours.

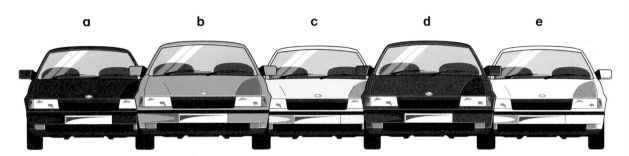

| a | b | c | d | e |

1. Brendan chose the darkest colour. What is the letter of the colour that he chose?
2. Saima liked light colours. Which two cars would she be most likely to chose between?
3. Put the colours in order starting with the darkest and ending with the lightest.

Bob made a list of all the pupils in his group.
This is how he wrote them down.

1. Write the names in alphabetical order. What was Bob's new list?
2. Count the number of letters in each name and write the list again in order of length with the shortest name first.
3. Which list do you think is more useful when the teacher checks who is absent?

Look back at your work in this lesson.
- How many different ways have you put things in order?
- What new words have you learnt?

③ Order and bar charts

Julie, Ali, Michael and Marie all have their 14th birthday this year. Julie's birthday is in March. Marie was born in August. Ali has his birthday in November. Michael was born in January.

Use the information about the birthday months to answer these questions.

1 Make a list of the girls' and boys' birthday months in the order in which they occur during the year.

2 Who is the eldest?

3 Name someone who is younger than Julie.

4 Who is older than Marie but younger than Michael?

Leanne has to arrange some new books on the bookshelf. The books have to be arranged in alphabetical order according to subjects. There are History, Science and French books already on the shelf.

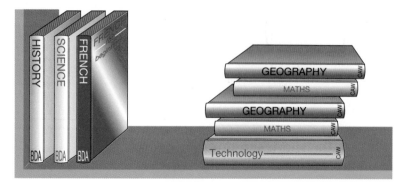

1 Draw the books already on the shelf in alphabetical order.

2 Between which books would Leanne put a Maths book?

3 Where would a Geography book go?

4 After Leanne had finished she was given a Technology book to put away. Where would she put the Technology book?

Here is a bar chart showing the number of books that were borrowed from the local children's library last week.

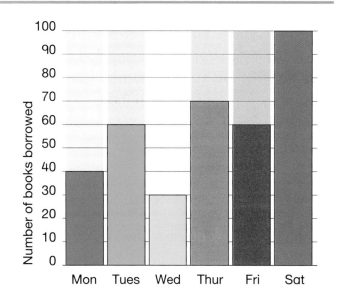

1 On which day were the most books taken out?
2 Can you think of a reason for this?
3 On which day were the fewest books borrowed?
4 Why do you think this could be?
5 On two of the days the same number of books were chosen. Which days were these?

Look at the number of books borrowed each day in exercise C.
1 Put the days in order starting with the one when most books were borrowed. Make sure that you write the number of how many books were borrowed beside each day.

Here is a pictogram showing the number of shapes in the shape box.

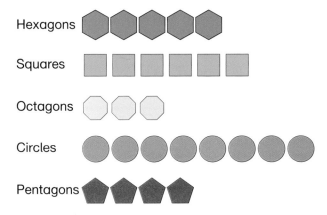

Hexagons

Squares

Octagons

Circles

Pentagons

1 Write down how many there are of each shape.
2 Which shape is there most of?
3 Are there more pentagons or more octagons?
4 Which shape has twice as many as the number of octagons?
5 Put the shapes in order of quantity.

Now look back at your work in this lesson.
• Can you use a calendar and the alphabet to put things in order?
• Can you use bar charts and pictograms to put information in order?

④ Doubling and halving

At parties glasses are not normally filled right to the brim. How many half-full glasses would there be from these full glasses?

Look at the following shapes.

1 How much of this shape is shaded?

2 Copy this shape on to squared paper and colour in half of it.

3 It is wrong to say 'half of this shape is shaded'. Why?

Ryan counted the shapes he had on his table. He lined them up in groups.

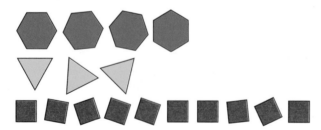

1 He put half of the squares away in the box.
How many are left on the table?

2 He took enough triangles out of the box to double the amount on the table.
How many triangles has he got now?

3 He made a pattern with the shapes and when he had finished he had half the hexagons left over.
How many hexagons did he use?

Give the answer to the following questions.

1 This stack is made with two bricks and is 10 cm tall.
How tall is one brick?

2 Jerry joins together two six-metre hoses to water the end
of his garden. How far will he be able to reach?

3 There are eight ice-creams on the rack. When half of them
have been sold, how many will be left?

Give the answer to the following questions.

1 Josh has eight football cards and Ali has ten. They decide to
put them together and share them equally. How many will
both have then?

2 Gill and Farah both have 23p left after an outing. If they put
their money together, how much will they be able to spend
on a bar of chocolate on the way home?

3 The cost of an adult theatre ticket is twice as much as a child's.
If it costs £3 for a child's ticket how much will it cost for an adult?

4 If two packets of crisps cost 40p how much does just one cost?

Here is a bar chart to show the number of chocolate bars
that were sold in a tuck shop in one week.

1 How many Milky Ways were sold?

2 Which chocolate bar was bought
by the same number of people as
the Milky Way?

3 One chocolate bar was half as
popular as two of the others.
Which one was this?

4 One chocolate bar was twice as
popular as two of the others.
Which was this? Was it the most
popular one?

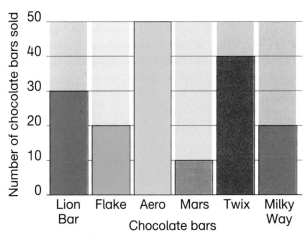

Now look back at your work in this lesson.
• Can you use bar charts to double things?
• Can you use pictures to show halves of things?

⑤ Comparing charts

What month do you think Suzanne Charlton was presenting this weather forecast?
Why do you think symbols are used in weather forecasts?

A

Here are the weather charts which show the weather for the last two weeks.

1. How many sunny days were there last week?
2. Were there more or fewer sunny days this week?
3. Which week had the most rainy days?
4. How many cloudy days are there altogether?

B

Here are two bar charts to show the number of babies born in a hospital during a two-week period.

1. How many babies were born on Monday of the first week?
2. In which week was the busiest Thursday?
3. How many more babies were born on Wednesday in the second week than in the first?
4. What was the total number of babies born at the weekend (Saturday and Sunday) during both weeks?

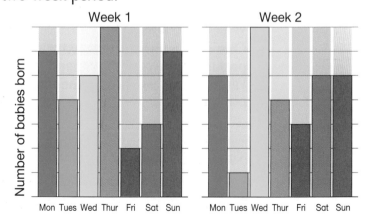

The chart on the right shows the number of pot plants that were sold by a garden centre in one week.

Number of plants sold

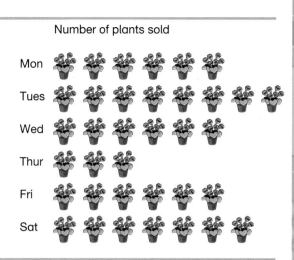

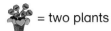 = two plants

1 How many plants were sold on Monday?
2 On which day were the fewest plants sold?
3 On three days the same number were sold. Which days were those?

Ali drew the garden centre's sales in exercise C in a different way.

= two plants

1 What are the three mistakes that he made?
2 On which day were the most plants sold?
3 How many more plants were sold on Tuesday than on Monday?

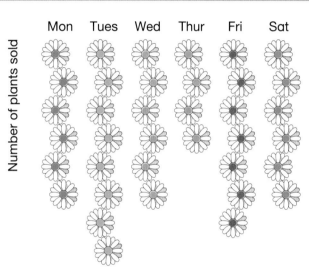

Number of plants sold

Several pupils had to buy their pets food last week. Three pupils bought food for their cats and three more for their dogs. The chart shows how much was spent on each pet.

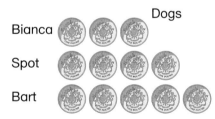

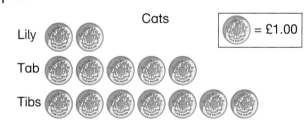

= £1.00

1 How much did it cost for Spot's food?
2 Tab and Tibs belong to the Smith family. How much does it cost the Smith family to feed them?
3 Which cat cost the most to feed?
4 How much was the cheapest bill?
5 Did the food for the cats cost more than the dogs', or less?

Now look back at your work in this lesson.
• Can you compare information from two charts?
• Can you gain more information by using two charts?

⑥ Bar chart skills

How many people in your
class like this drink?

Copy this list of the fruit drinks flavours.

Flavour	Sales
Orange	
Lemon	
Lime	
Blackcurrant	
Raspberry	
Strawberry	
Vanilla	

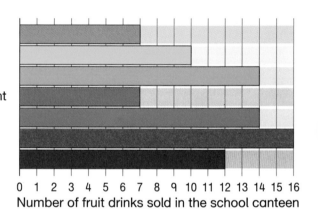

Number of fruit drinks sold in the school canteen

1 Use the bar chart to fill in the sales column.

Use your results to answer these questions.
2 Which flavour was the most popular?
3 Were there more blackcurrant or more raspberry drinks sold?
4 How many more strawberry than raspberry drinks were sold?

Here is a graph to show how many
people went to change their books
at the mobile library last week.

1 50 people went on Thursday and 80
on Tuesday. Copy the chart and fill
in the number of people for Tuesday
and Thursday.
2 Write the days in the order of the
number of people, starting with
the busiest.

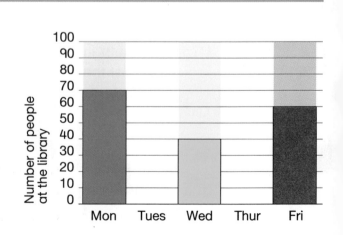

Mr Jones has two daughters and three sons. Mr Peters has a son and a daughter. Mr Martin has two sons and a daughter. Mr Ali has four daughters and a son. Mr Short has a son.

Name	Boys	Girls

1 Copy and fill in this table with the fathers' names. Write the names in alphabetical order. Then write the numbers of children each man has in the correct column.

The pupils in Year 5 conducted a survey of their class to find out what kinds of house they lived in. The results are shown here in a pictogram.

Flat

Bungalow

Terraced house

Semi-detached house

Detached house

1 Draw a bar chart of these results in your book. Put them in order of the type of home in which the largest number of pupils live.

Now look back at your work in this lesson.
- Can you read and draw bar charts to show information?
- Do you prefer bar charts or lists with numbers?

Module **A**3

Number and measurement

❶ Calculator sums
Using a calculator to solve problems where the numbers are too big or awkward

❷ Doubling numbers
Doubling numbers may be all you need to do

❸ Estimating
Guessing the number of things in a place

❹ Choosing measurements
Deciding what measures to use

❺ Matching
Matching things to fit and the days of the week and the dates they fall on

❻ Number skills
Matching, estimating and doubling to solve problems

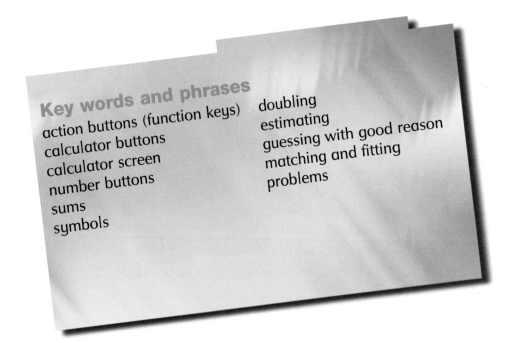

Key words and phrases

action buttons (function keys)
calculator buttons
calculator screen
number buttons
sums
symbols

doubling
estimating
guessing with good reason
matching and fitting
problems

① Calculator sums

How many keys (buttons) does your calculator have altogether?
There are more buttons and switches in this aeroplane's cockpit than the pilot needs at any one time.
How many symbols can the screen show?
What other features does the calculator have?

 Work out these sums using your calculator. Here is an example.

1	37 + 18 =	6	2 + 18 =
2	double 55 =	7	67 + 88 =
3	double 23 =	8	74 + 95 =
4	52 + 54 =	9	68 + 75 =
5	42 + 35 =	10	62 + 84 =

 Do these sums on the calculator. Copy them and write in the answers.

1	56 - 28 =	6	64 - 18 =
2	67 - 32 =	7	93 - 27 =
3	54 - 33 =	8	64 - 59 =
4	82 - 70 =	9	81 - 57 =
5	79 - 46 =	10	98 - 12 =

 Write these problems as sums in your book and then use the calculator to answer them.

1 Paul has £23 saved. He earns £13. How much has he now?
2 Daniel has won £40 on the school raffle. He has £24 saved. How much money has he now?
3 Shauna is given £37 for her birthday. She has £65 in the bank. How much money has she got now?
4 David's gran offers to double the money in his piggy bank. He counts it out and he has £16. How much will he have after his gran's visit?
5 Jemma and Tanya put their money together to buy a CD player. Jemma has £76 and Tanya has £68. How much do the girls have altogether?

D

Look at the items on sale. Lisa has £50 to spend and she wants to buy two items. Use the calculator to check if she can afford to buy the items in each question.

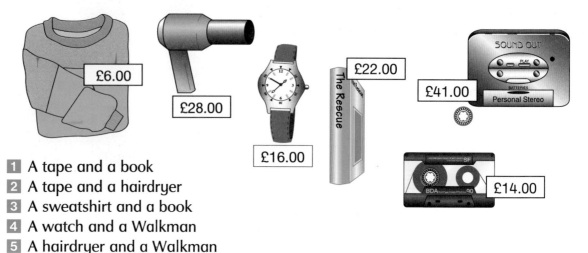

£6.00

£28.00

£22.00

£41.00

SOUND OUT
PLAY
BATTERIES
Personal Stereo

£16.00

The Rescue

£14.00

SF
BDA 90

1. A tape and a book
2. A tape and a hairdryer
3. A sweatshirt and a book
4. A watch and a Walkman
5. A hairdryer and a Walkman

E

Write these problems as sums and solve them using the calculator.

1. Gill had 67 wristbands. She loses a box with 23 in. How many has she now?
2. Paul had £67 saved. He buys a pair of trainers costing £48. How much money has he left?
3. There are 96 people on a train. At the next station 37 people get off. How many are left on the train?
4. A traffic jam is 26 cars long. Soon 18 more cars join it. How many are in the queue now?
5. So far Year 8 has collected £98 in sponsor money. Then 8J hands in £48. How much has Year 8 collected now?

F

Write these problems as sums and solve them.

1. There are 46 people at the local football game. A coach of 64 people arrives. How many are there now?
2. Donna has 59 pop magazines. Mark gives her 62 more. How many has she now?
3. Shane has saved programmes from concerts. He had 34 but then lost a bag with 18 of them in. How many has he now?
4. Hannah has 27 felt-tipped pens but the teacher's box has double that number. How many felt tips are in the teacher's box?
5. Luke has 48 biscuits in the tin. He puts 27 out on a plate. How many are left in the tin?

Now look back at your work in this lesson.
- Do you know the important buttons on the calculator?
- Can you add up and take away using a calculator?

② Doubling numbers

There are equal numbers of lamp posts on both sides of this road. How many lamp posts are there altogether? How many lamp shades are there altogether?

A Double each of these numbers in your head without working them out on the page.

1 6
2 1
3 9
4 4
5 3

6 8
7 7
8 0
9 5
10 2

B Write down which sums are RIGHT and which are WRONG.

1 Double 6 is 13
2 8 and 8 = 16
3 Twice 4 = 10
4 Double 7 is 14
5 Two threes = 5

6 Double 9 is 20
7 5 twice = 10
8 Two 2s = 5
9 Double 0 is 0
10 1 + 1 = 3

C Write these problems as sums in your book and solve them.

1 One row of seats at a cinema sits eight people. How many people can sit in two rows of seats?
2 One strip contains seven stamps. How many stamps are there in two strips?
3 One table at a café can seat five people. How many people can sit at two tables?
4 James gets £6 pocket money. He did so well in his maths test last Friday that his dad doubled it. How much did he get?
5 There are three pairs of socks in the wash basket. How many single socks are there?

Paul has to deliver coffee to offices on each side of the corridor.
He counts the doors down one side and doubles the total to
find the number of cups he needs. This is how he works out his
deliveries for each floor.

1 Paul has made some mistakes. Copy this table but correct Paul's
mistakes in the Cups Needed column.

Floor	Doors on one side	Cups needed
1	9	19
2	6	12
3	7	14
4	8	18
5	5	11

Look at the pictures below. How many would be in each picture
if the number were doubled?

Saida sowed some flowers in spring last year. She counted them
carefully. This year there was double the number of flowers in
each row. Here are pictures of the rows this year. How many
plants did she plant in each row last year?

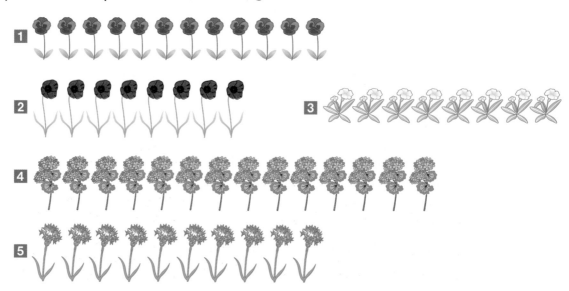

Now look back at your work in this lesson.
- Did you manage to work out the questions in your head?
- What kind of question is the most difficult?

❸ Estimating

Can you guess about how many penguins there are in the photo without counting them one by one? Discuss your method of estimating.

Look at each of these pictures and say for each question whether **a** or **b** has more items.

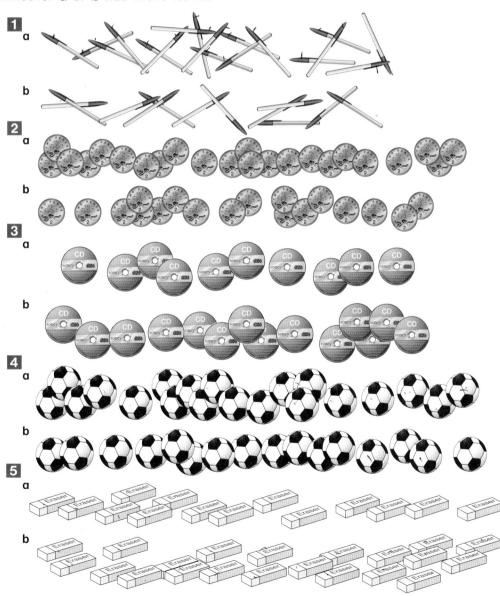

B

Make a good guess whether there are more than 20 items in each question. Do not count them! Say 'more' or 'less'.

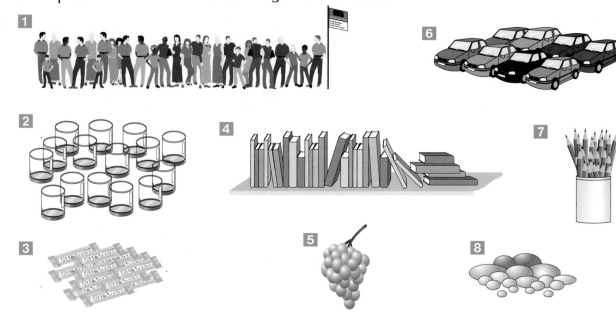

C

Make a good guess about how many there are in each picture.
Do not count them! Use the numbers below the pictures to help you.

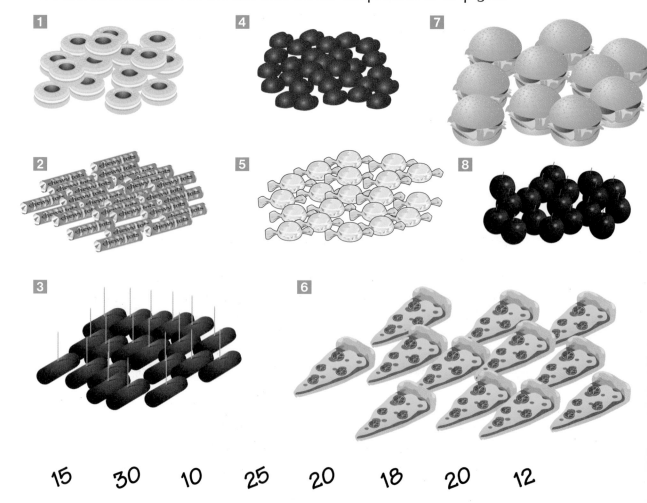

15   30   10   25   20   18   20   12

Estimate how many items are in each picture. Do not count them!

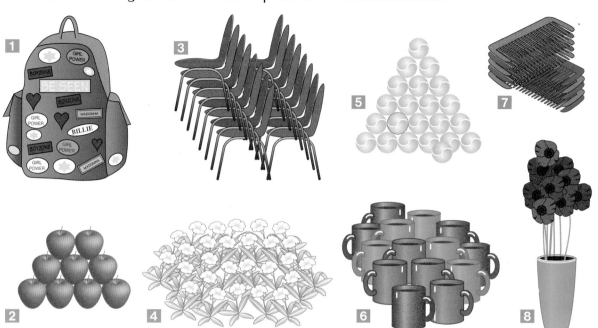

You will need a calculator and a set of playing cards.
Take all the picture cards and all the hearts and put them
back in the box. Draw up a table like this in your book.

Estimate	Count	Difference

1 Spread a handful of cards on the table and guess how many
there are. Put this number in the Estimate column.

2 Now count the cards and put this number in the Count column.

3 Find out how close your estimate is to the real number. Put the
bigger number in to your calculator first and take away the
other number. Put the answer from your calculator in the
Difference column. This difference column tells you how good
your guess was. If it is a small number it was a good guess!

Now look back at your work in this lesson.
- Are your estimating skills getting better?
- What new words have you learned in this lesson?

④ Choosing measurements

The bus driver said two of the objects in the picture were too long to go in the bus. Without using your ruler which are the two longest objects?

Look at these lines. Use the tools your teacher gives you to find out which line is the longest in each question. When you know the answer write it in your book.

Line_____ is the longest. I found this out by using _____.

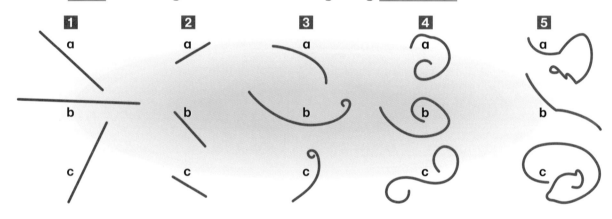

Paul wants to know which office has the tallest plant. He stands next to the plant in each office and marks its height on his sketch.

Copy room plant   Mrs Ullah's   Mrs Simmons'   Mr Jackson's   Mr Lang's

1 Which office has the tallest plant?
2 Which office has the shortest plant?
3 Write the offices in order of plant size starting with the shortest plant and ending with the tallest plant.

What is shorter than you?

1 Look around the classroom and choose five things which are shorter than you (e.g. a desk, a table, a chair, a bookcase, a small filing cabinet). Now copy this table and complete the first column.

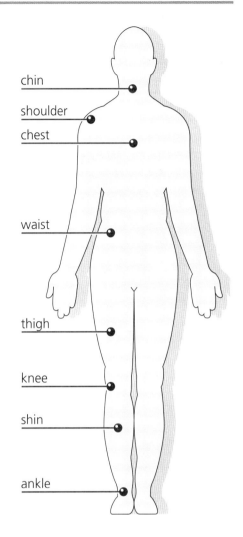

chin
shoulder
chest
waist
thigh
knee
shin
ankle

Things	Nearly as high as
1	
2	
3	
4	
5	

2 Copy this sketch of the human body. Stand up straight next to each thing in number 1.
Fill in the second column of the table with where things come to on you.

3 Which is the tallest thing?

4 Which is the shortest thing?

5 Write all the things in order starting with the shortest and ending with the tallest.

Estimate the longest and the shortest.

1 Look at all the things that people in your class are using to write with, such as pens and pencils. Who is writing with the longest thing?

2 Look at the pencil cases in your classroom. Who has got the shortest pencil case?

Think about measuring distances.

1 Which toilets are closest to your classroom, the boys' or the girls'?

2 How could you measure this to show someone who did not agree with you?

3 Which is the longest corridor in your school?

4 How could you measure this to show someone who did not agree with you?

5 Talk to your teacher about your measuring ideas and ask if you may do the measuring.

Lee's team has been given a set of measuring tasks. They can choose one thing to help them measure for each task. Which would you choose (**a**, **b** or **c**) to help you with each task?

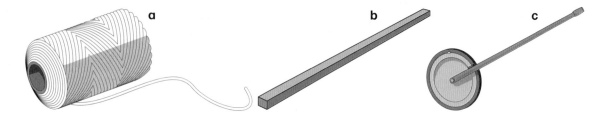

1 Find out who is the tallest person in your team.

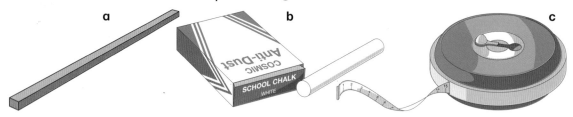

2 Find out who has the longest jump.

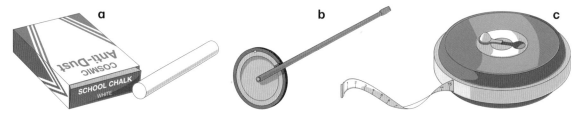

3 Find out who can throw the ball the furthest.

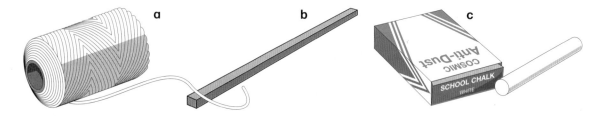

4 Find out who has the longest arm.

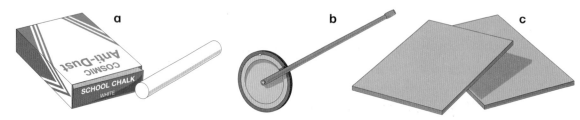

5 Find out who could fit through the thinnest gap.

Now look back at your work in this lesson.
- What was the most helpful thing you used for measuring? Why?
- Can you now measure height, length and width?

⑤ Matching

Finding the perfect match for someone can often be difficult. How often do you think Cilla succeeds?

Saida has labelled the keys to match the order of the lockers.

1. Which key will open locker 4?
2. Which key will open locker 2?
3. Which key will open locker 8?
4. Which key will open locker 5?
5. Which key will open locker 10?
6. Which key will open locker 3?
7. Which key will open locker 7?
8. Which key will open locker 6?

Saida gives the keys to her classmates. They each need to work out which is their locker.

1. Which locker does key H open?
2. Which locker does key I open?
3. Which locker does key D open?
4. Which locker does key E open?
5. Which locker does key G open?
6. Which locker does key J open?
7. Which locker does key C open?
8. Which locker does key B open?

C

Jackie's birthday is on June 10th. She works out that her birthday will be on a Saturday this year.
What day of the week will these dates be?

1 June 13th
2 June 8th
3 June 17th
4 June 15th
5 June 6th

6 June 5th
7 June 9th
8 June 20th
9 June 7th
10 June 19th

D

Jackie plans a party on her birthday. She has a job to do on each day of the week before the party.
Add the missing date to each of these notes to remind Jackie what to do.

1 Monday June _____: Phone friends

2 Friday June _____: Make food

3 Tuesday June _____: Borrow Ann's CD

4 Thursday June _____: Move Mum's ornaments

5 Wednesday June _____: Buy drinks

6 Sunday June _____: Buy new dress

E

Beth drives a truck as her job. She notices the car number plates as she drives along. She knows that the letter at the start of the plate tells the year the car was made.

She remembers that E is 1987 because this is the year of her truck.
Look at these number plates. Which year was each of these cars made?

1 D167 RTH
2 B782 NHL
3 G778 RDA
4 C639 VNG
5 A842 TCF

6 B453 WDS
7 E224 LLH
8 F563 DEF
9 H821 LIK
10 C334 SFE

Paul has to deliver mail on the fifth floor of an office block.
All the office numbers on this floor start with 5.
The first is 5A, the second 5B, and so on.

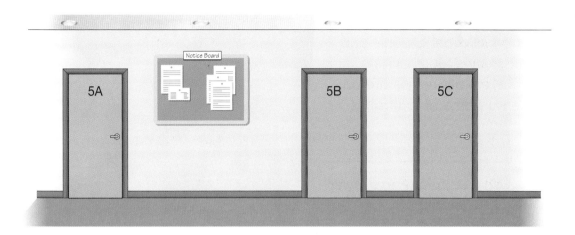

He wants to sort the mail so that he can deliver it quickly.
He puts all the letters for office 5A in slot 1 ready to post.

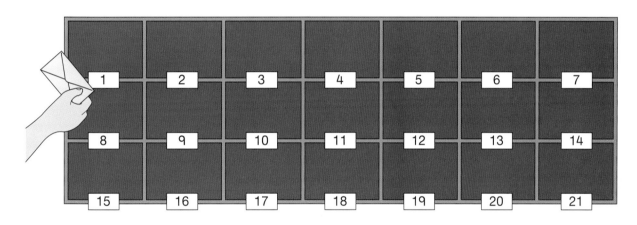

Which office will get the letters that Paul places in these slots?

1 Slot 3   **4** Slot 6

2 Slot 7   **5** Slot 10

3 Slot 14

In which slot should Paul put letters for these offices?

6 For office 5C?   **9** For office 5F?

7 For office 5G?   **10** For office 5D?

8 For office 5B?

Now look back at your work in this lesson.
- Can you match numbers with letters in order?
- Can you match the numbers of days of the week with their names?

⑥ Number skills

Do you have a favourite footballer?
What number shirt does he wear?
What number do you get if you add
the numbers on Michael Owen's and
Alan Shearer's shirts together?
How many players altogether are on
the field when a game of football is
played?

A Use a calculator to answer
these questions.

1. 54 + 23 =
2. 67 + 28 =
3. 65 - 34 =
4. 84 - 47 =
5. double 37 =
6. double 63 =
7. Lee saved £59. He already had £26. How much money has he now?
8. Lucia had £37. She spent £18. How much money has she left?
9. Jack wins £15 on the slot machine. He presses the chance button
   and wins double. How much money will he get now?
10. There are 67 people on the coach. Then 36 people get off at the
    next stop. How many are left on the coach?

B Estimating means guessing roughly how many items there are.
In these questions do not count the items. Just by looking, write
whether there are more or less than 10 in each.

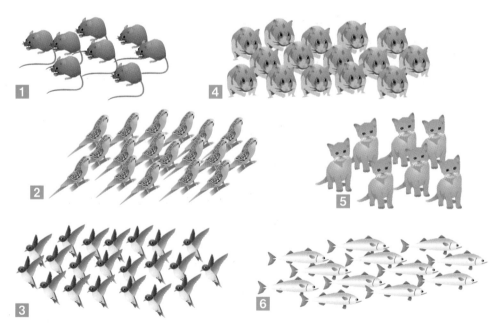

Do not count these collections. Write whether there are 'nearly 10' or 'nearly 20'.

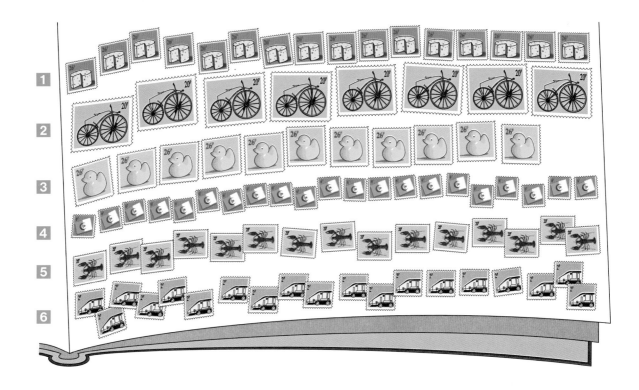

Do each of these questions in your head without using a calculator. Write the answer down in your book.

1. double 5
2. double 8
3. double 3
4. Is this sum correct? Double 9 = 17
5. Is this sum correct? Double 6 = 12
6. Is this sum correct? Double 2 = 6
7. How many would be in this box if the number was doubled?

$$\boxed{4}$$

8. How many would be in this box if the number was doubled?

$$\boxed{1}$$

9. How many would be in this box if the number was doubled?

$$\boxed{7}$$

10. How many would be in this box if the number was doubled?

$$\boxed{9}$$

E

Beth, the truck driver, is painting a sign on her truck. Each letter is going to be a different colour.

1 Which letter will take up the least paint?

F

Rachel helps in the library in the school holidays.
The number of the shelf and the author's name are linked.
Shelf 12 is for names starting with **A**, shelf 13 is for **B** and so on.

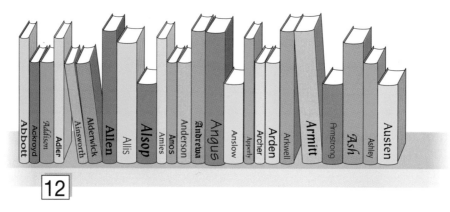

Abbott Ackroyd Addison Adler Ainsworth Aldenwick Allen Allis Alsop Amies Amos Anderson Andrew Angus Anslow Apperly Archer Arden Arkwell Armitt Armstrong Ash Ashley Austen

12

1 Which names will go on shelf 15?
2 Which names will go on shelf 18?
3 Which names will go on shelf 20?
4 Which names will go on shelf 17?
5 Which names will go on shelf 22?
6 Which shelf will a book by Jones go on?
7 Which shelf will a book by Banks go on?
8 Which shelf will a book by Davis go on?
9 Which shelf will a book by Fox go on?
10 Which shelf will a book by Moon go on?

Now look back at your work in this lesson.
• Can you use a calculator to work out sums?
• Can you match letters and numbers in order?

Shape and space

❶ Describing shapes

Talking about shapes helps to make the differences clear. Using words like *shape, curve* and *straight, oval* and *circular, flat* and *rounded*

❷ Describing parts of drawings

Matching parts of real things, like furniture, with part of the drawings is important, even if you do not know the names of these parts

❸ Right angles

Finding right angles everywhere in real life and in pictures

❹ Shapes and drawings

Talking about shapes within drawings

❺ Angles in drawings

Finding out whether angles in drawings are greater or lesser than right angles

❻ Shape and space skills

Solving problems about real things may require drawing and talking about them, recognising angles and lines

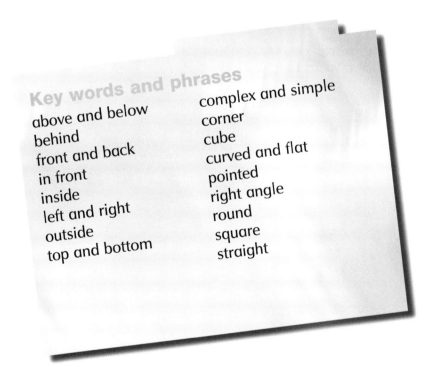

Key words and phrases

above and below
behind
front and back
in front
inside
left and right
outside
top and bottom

complex and simple
corner
cube
curved and flat
pointed
right angle
round
square
straight

1 Describing shapes

What lines can you see here that are curved? Can you see any straight lines? Are there any round or pointed objects? Are the surfaces flat or uneven?

---

1 Look at the picture. Find shapes that can be described by the words in the box.

curved	round	straight	flat	pointed

2 What other words can you use which have the same meaning as *curved*?

3 What other words can you use for *flat*?

4 Look around you, in the classroom or outside. Write down two things that are straight.

5 Write down two things that are pointed.

6 Write down two things that are round.

Copy these sentences. Use the words you used in exercise A to complete them. You can use a word twice or not at all.

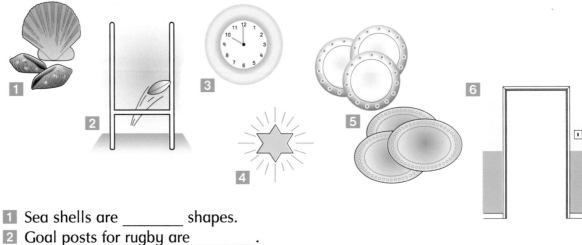

1 Sea shells are _____ shapes.

2 Goal posts for rugby are _____.

3 A clock face is _____.

4 This star is _____.

5 Some plates are _____ and others are oval.

6 The carpenter made sure the door frame was _____.

Which picture is being described?

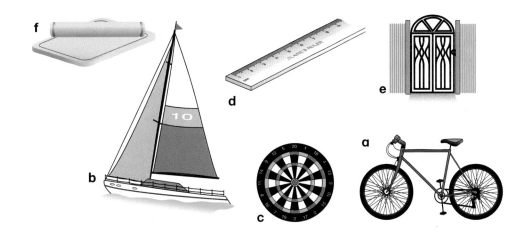

1. The pastry will be rolled out on a flat surface.
2. The wheels on this are round.
3. This sails on the sea and is pointed at the bow.
4. We throw darts at a round target.
5. You use this to draw a straight line.
6. This is opened and closed and is curved at the top.

 Look at the lines being pointed to in the picture. Say if they are straight or curved.

Make a list of the items that you can see on this dressing table that are these shapes.

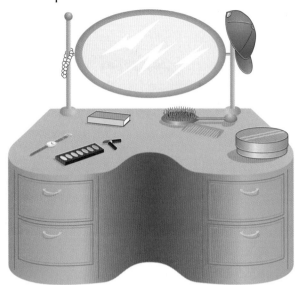

1 Curved
2 Round
3 Straight

Copy these sentences and use the words *straight*, *curved*, *round*, *flat* to complete them.

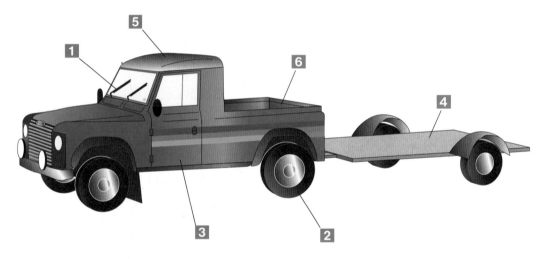

1 The windscreen wipers are _____.
2 The wheels are _____.
3 The stripes are _____.
4 The trailer is _____ to carry the hay.
5 The roof of the cab is _____.
6 The tailgate is _____.

Now look back at your work in this lesson.
- Think about the different things around you. Do they mostly have straight or curved edges?
- What are the most useful words for describing shapes?

② **Describing parts of drawings**

How many things in this picture are on top of something else?

In the picture find the following things.

1 Something on the top of something
2 Something at the bottom of something
3 Something inside something
4 Something in front of something
5 Something behind something

Where are the arrows pointing? Copy and complete the sentences.

1. The roots are at the _____ of the tree.
2. The star is at the _____ of the box.
3. The man is looking at the bird on _____ of the wall.
4. The notice is pinned at the _____ of the board.
5. The arrow is pointing to the _____ of the chair.
6. There is a hole at the _____ of the bucket.

Use the words *under* or *over* to describe what is happening.

1. The bus is going _____ the bridge.
2. The horse jumps _____ the fence.
3. The plane flies _____ the trees.
4. The tunnel goes _____ the river.
5. The potatoes grow _____ the ground.
6. You can see the big wheel _____ the heads of the people.

Here are some runners in a race.

1 Who is running in front of Rachel?
2 Who is behind Sam?
3 Who is in front of Asif?
4 Who is running behind Wayne?
5 Sara is running behind all the pupils. Who is running in the front of them all?

Look carefully at the picture and describe the positions of the following, using the words you have learnt in this lesson.

1 The cars are on _____ of the bridge, and the river is _____ .
2 The light is on _____ of the police car, and the street lamp is _____ the car.
3 The man is at the _____ of the ladder, and the sun is shining _____ .
4 The bus is _____ the police car, and the red car is _____ the bus.

Now look back at your work in this lesson.
- Do you know how to describe where things are in a drawing?
- What do you think are the most useful words for describing things?

③ Right angles

Some of these corners form right angles, some do not. Can you tell which ones are right angles?

What is a right angle?

1 Name two objects which have right angles.

2 Place two straight thin objects such as a pencil or a straw on the page.
Turn one away from the other to make a right angle.
Draw the angle in your book and label it right angle.

3 Draw another right angle, open in a different direction.

4 Check your drawing with a corner of a book or another square corner.

5 Draw an angle which is wider than a right angle, by eye.

6 Draw an angle which is narrower than a right angle, by eye.
Then check your estimate.

Use a square of paper or a cube to decide which of the following angles are right angles.

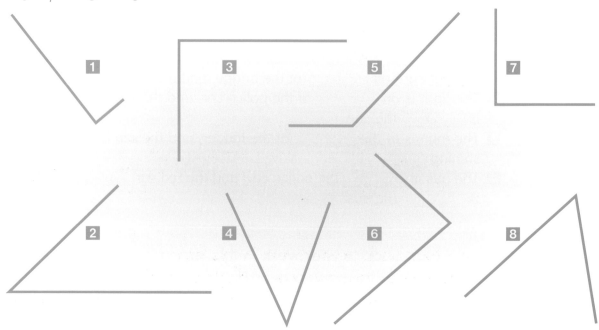

All of these things have corners.

a 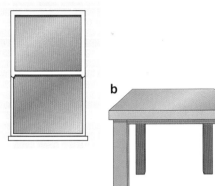

c d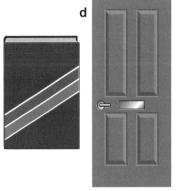

e

b

1 Copy the pictures above and show as many right angles as you can find. Mark each of the right angles with a square corner. Here is an example.

 Draw some more angles.
1 Draw two right angles.
2 Draw two narrower angles.
3 Draw two wide angles.

 Look carefully at the pictures below and say whether the angle marked is a right angle or not.

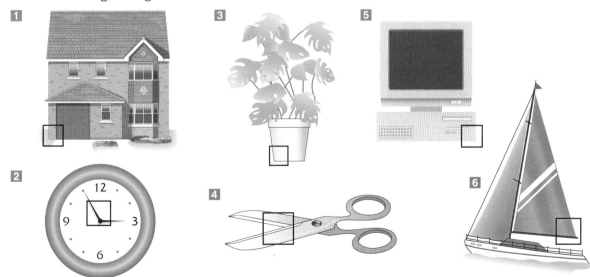

Now look back at your work in this lesson.
- Can you recognise a right angle by eye?
- How do you check whether a corner really is a right angle?

④ Shapes and drawings

What shapes do you see in
this picture?

Look at the picture.
1. What parts of the Viking ship are curved?
2. Are there any straight lines in the picture?
3. What is the difference between the rim line of the shield
   and the ropes?
4. What is the opposite to the bottom of something? What is
   the opposite to the front?

Copy and complete the sentences. Use words such as *curve*,
straight and *rounded*, as well as *bottom* and *top*.

1. A finger print is made up of many _____ lines.
2. The _____ of a test tube is curved and the _____
   and sides are straight.
3. The Union Jack is made up from _____ lines.
4. The sign for the carpet sale is _____.
5. The footprint makes _____ patterns in the sand, and the
   toes are an _____ shape.

C Look at the picture of the bungalow. Use words from the box to answer these questions.

above	under	behind
on top	at the bottom	
below	in front	over

1 Where are the trees?
2 Where are the flower beds?
3 Where is the chimney?
4 Where are the clouds?
5 What do you see in the picture that has straight lines?
6 Where can you see curved or rounded shapes?

D Look at this picture of a cycle race.

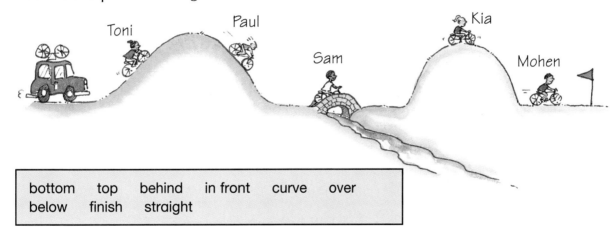

Toni   Paul   Kia   Sam   Mohen

bottom	top	behind	in front	curve	over
below	finish	straight			

1 Use the words from the box above to help you write a description of the race.

E Answer these questions about the bicycle race.
1 Who is going over the bridge?
2 Who is at the top of the last hill?
3 Where is the support vehicle?
4 Who is in front of the support vehicle?
5 Who is at the bottom of the final hill, and going along the straight to the finish?
6 Who is behind Sam, and who is in front of Sam?

Now look back at your work in this lesson.
* Can you talk about the shapes in drawings?
* What words do you use to describe shapes in drawings?

⑤ Angles in drawings

There are two types of joints – simple joints and slanted joints.

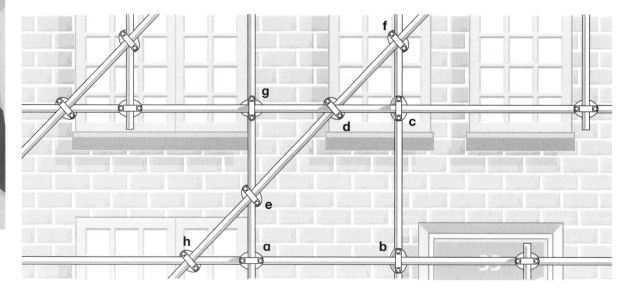

Look at the picture of the scaffolding.
1. Which are the simple joints?
2. What kind of angles do the simple joints have?
3. How can you check that an angle is less or more than a right angle?
4. Use tracing paper to draw the lines between **a**, **b**, **c**, **d** and **e**.
   How many sides has this shape?
5. Mark the right angles on that shape.
6. Find another shape and copy it in your book.

Some of these shapes have right angles, some do not.
Use a square of paper or a cube to check the angle.

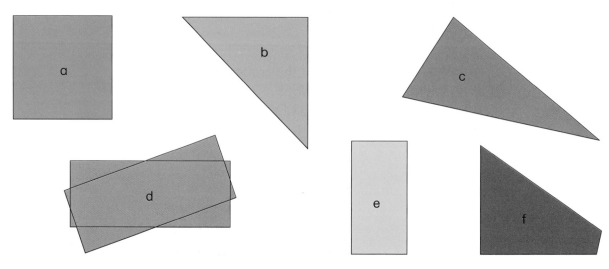

1. Copy the shapes that have right angles.
2. Mark the right angles with a cross.

Look at this hockey pitch.

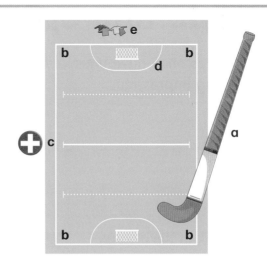

1 Describe the shape of the hockey stick. (**a**)
2 Name the angles marked. (**b**)
3 Where is the nurse sitting? (**c**)
4 Describe the shape marked. (**d**)
5 Write a sentence to describe where the jumpers have been thrown. (**e**)

This is a map of some roads in a town. Notice how Church Street is at right angles to Oak Road. Which other junctions are right angles?

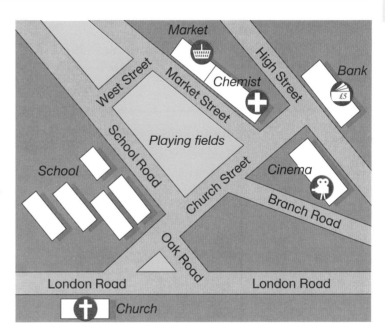

1 School Road is at right angles to _____ and _____.
2 The High Street is at right angles to _____.
3 Oak Road is at right angles to _____.
4 Which right angle is nearer the top of the map?
5 Which corner at the bottom of the map is narrower than a right angle?

Describe the position of these buildings.
6 The bank
7 The school
8 The _____ is next to the chemist.
9 The cinema is on the corner of _____ Street and _____ Street.

Now look back at your work in this lesson.
- Look around and see how many right angles you can find.
- Do you have difficulty telling whether an angle is less than or more than a right angle?

⑥ Shape and space skills

Modern sculptures often have unusual forms which give strong impressions.

 Look at the picture.
1. How many curved edges can you see?
2. How many straight edges can you see?
3. How many right angles can you find in the picture?

 Think about lines.

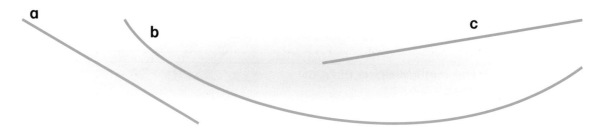

1. Draw three different straight lines of different lengths.
2. Draw three different curved lines.
3. Copy the lines above and label them *straight* or *curved*.

 Look at this picture.
1. What objects have right angles? How do you know that?
2. What other right angles do you think there are in the room, even if you cannot see them?
3. Open your book at right angles. How can you check that it is a right angle?

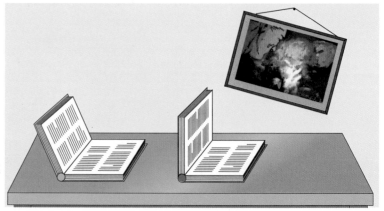

Think about these shapes.

1 Draw around any circular thing, for example a paper cup.

2 Use a right angle corner to draw a rectangle or a square inside it like this.

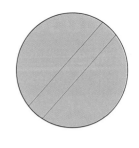

Look carefully at the picture. Copy these sentences, and fill in the missing words from the word box. Not all the words are used and some words may be used more than once.

over	under	on top	right angle	above	in front
behind	round	straight	curve	rectangle	

1 The clock face is _____. The time says three o'clock. The hands on the clock are at _____ angles.

2 The cat is asleep _____ of the cupboard. The books and the lamp are on _____ of the cupboard. The corners of the cupboard are _____ _____.

3 The armchair has _____ sides, and a _____ back.

4 The mat on the floor is a _____ shape.

5 The pictures are _____ the armchair, and each picture has square corners which are called _____ _____.

6 The sound system is built up by putting square units _____ of each other. Each corner is a _____ angle. There are _____ buttons to operate the system.

Now look back at your work in this lesson.
- Do you see any lines around you that are neither straight nor round?
- What else can you think of that is a square or rectangle shape?

Module **A**1–**A**4

Practise your skills

Number

1 Write the numbers of these raffle tickets in order, smallest first.

2 Which two numbers are missing?

3 Copy and fill in the hidden or missing numbers.

   a 37   38   ☺   ☺   43   44

   b ☺   78   ☺   37   81   82

4 Harry wants to buy a large balloon. Which coins will he need?

Small balloon 42p
Large balloon 86p

5 Harry changes his mind and wants only a small balloon. Which coins will he need?

Handling data

1 Here is a bar chart of how pupils from two classes came to school today.

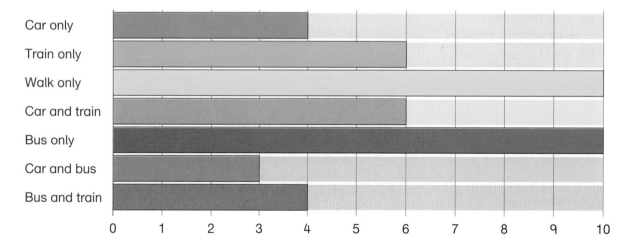

Make a list of the number of pupils for each type of transport.

Transport	Number of pupils
1	
2	
3	
4	
5	
6	
7	

2 Which transport was the most common?
3 Which is the least common?
4 How many people in total used a bus on its own, or with a car, or with a train?
5 How many people used a car on its own or with a train or with a bus?

Number
1 Write the answers after working these out in your head.
a   30 +6 =
b   10+ 40 +5 =

Use a calculator to do these questions.

2 55 + 39 =
3 double 28 =
4 Jerry saved £18. He already had £66. How much money has he now?
5 There are 47 seats in the school coach. There are already 16 pupils inside it. Can a class of 28 pupils all get in?

Shape and space
Use tracing paper to copy these pictures. Draw in the other half.

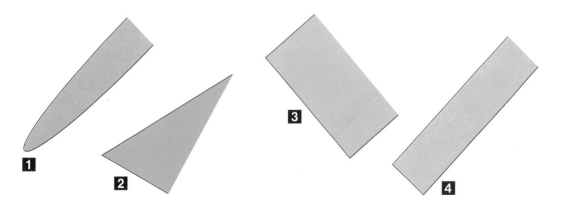

5 What things in the picture have curved lines?

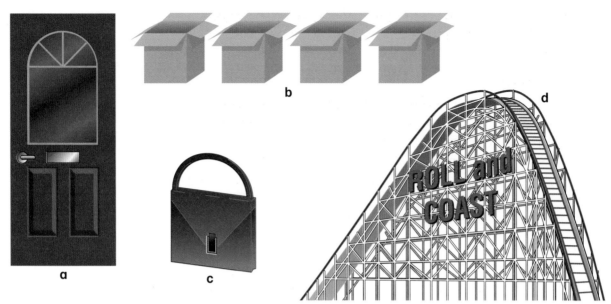

6 What things have straight lines?

7 How many right angles can you find?

8 Certain things in the picture have handles to hold them with.
How many handles can you see?

9 Which of these three piles of books will take the least space on the shelf?

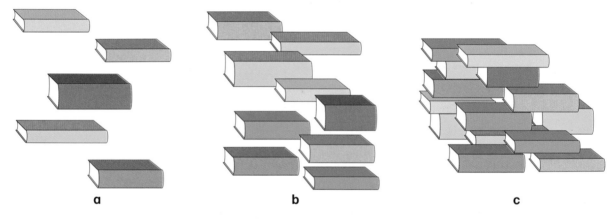

a   b   c

10 Which will take the most space?

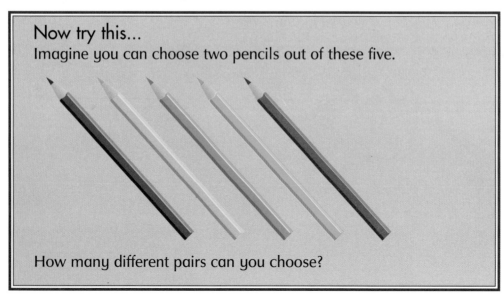

Now try this...
Imagine you can choose two pencils out of these five.

How many different pairs can you choose?

Check your skills

You can check how well you can do the things listed here. Get your parents and friends to help check them. Your teacher will give you a copy of this page to tick on.

Numbers and money

1 I can read and write numbers up to 100 and put them in order. ☐

2 I can enter numbers into a calculator correctly, add and subtract them to solve problems like the cost of two things. ☐

3 I know which of two numbers is bigger than the other. ☐

4 I can add tens numbers like 60 to a units number like 8 without pen and paper. ☐

5 I can choose the right coins to make any amount less then £1. ☐

Measurements and matching

1 I can find the half-way mark inside things just by looking at them. ☐

2 I can double small numbers without pen and paper. ☐

3 I can guess the number of things on a table or in the playground without counting them. ☐

4 I can use handwidths or height to compare the size of things. ☐

5 I can put things in order such as size or number, and can match things in one set with things in another set by their order. ☐

Finding out about things

1 I can find things about what people do and how things are and record them in an orderly way. ☐

2 I can understand bar charts and change them into tables of numbers. ☐

3 I can compare two charts and find more information. ☐

4 I can draw bits of bar charts. ☐

Shapes and drawings

1 I can understand words like *curve* and *straight*, *oval* and *circular*, *flat* and *rounded*. ☐

2 I can understand drawings of objects such as furniture and find which parts of them relate to parts of the real things they show. ☐

3 I can find right angles everywhere in real life and in pictures and know which angles are greater or lesser than right angles. ☐

Module Ⓐ5

Number and measurement

❶ Estimating time
Figuring out roughly how many seconds, minutes or hours it takes to do something in daily life

❷ Digital clocks
Telling the time by digital clocks

❸ Measuring time without the clock
Finding which of two things takes longer, using our own sense of time

❹ Ordering lengths
Judging visually whether something is longer or shorter and smaller or larger

❺ Comparing lengths
Using different units for comparison

❻ Measurement skills
Comparing sizes and times

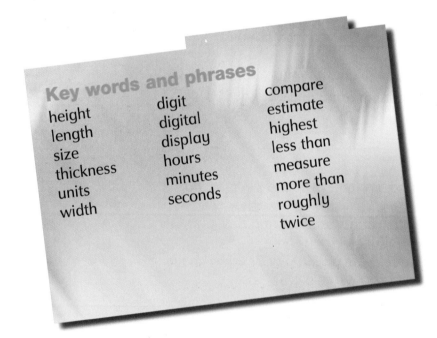

Key words and phrases

height	digit	compare
length	digital	estimate
size	display	highest
thickness	hours	less than
units	minutes	measure
width	seconds	more than
		roughly
		twice

① **Estimating time**

What activities can you see in these pictures?
Have you done any of these activities yourself?
Everything we do takes some time, sometimes
a long time, sometimes a short time.

Do the three tasks in numbers 1–3. This is not a race. They will
help you to understand time. Start and finish each task when
the teacher tells you. Then do number 4.

1 Imagine you are sticking a decorative tape all around the edge
of your table or desk. You have to gently press it down with your
fingers all around the edge. Take turns if you share your table
with others.

2 Sit still with hands folded and without talking. You may read.

3 Write down the numbers starting 2, 4, 6, ..., ... until your teacher
tells you to stop.

4 Make a list of the three tasks in the order of time they took. Put
the longest first.

Copy and complete the sentences by filling in the gaps using one of these phrases from the word box.

takes seconds	takes minutes	takes hours

60 seconds = 1 minute
60 minutes = 1 hour

1 To brush your teeth _____.
2 To write your name _____.
3 To get from home to school _____.
4 To cross the English channel by ferry _____.
5 To tidy your room _____.
6 To cook a pizza _____.
7 To wash the car _____.
8 To get a six on a dice _____.

Think about familiar tasks.
1 Write down two tasks that take a few seconds to do.
2 Write down two tasks that take a few minutes to do.
3 Write down two tasks that take a few hours to do.

Copy these sentences and fill in the missing words using one of these words.

hours	minutes	seconds

1 Lynn took more than a _____ to pack her bag for school.
2 Vijay set off on a 40 km bike ride, after breakfast. After about an _____ he stopped for a few _____ to have a break and a drink, then completed his journey. It took him _____ to get home.
3 James was late for football. It took him about 30 _____ to wash and brush his hair before he left his house.
4 Aimee wrote her timetable in her homework diary. It took her about 20 _____ to finish.
5 Hasan ran 100 metres in 15 _____.
6 Sara entered a sponsored walk and spent 5 _____ to cover 15 miles.

Now look back at your work in this lesson.
• Can you estimate how long you spent on each section?
• How many seconds are there in a minute? How many minutes in an hour?

② Digital clocks

Digital clocks are everywhere. Do you think they are easier to use than other types of clock?

Think about digital clocks.
1. Name three places where you have seen digital clocks.
2. Do all the digital clocks have four spaces to show digits?
3. Most digital clocks have a marker like this : in the middle. Why is that needed?
4. What is the latest time shown on the clocks in the picture?
5. What is the earliest time?

Draw a rectangle like this to show a 24 hour digital clock. It must have two boxes for the hours and two boxes for the minutes.

1. True or false?
   The left-hand box for hours uses only three different digits: 1   2   3.
2. List all the digits the right-hand box for hours needs.
3. List all the digits the left-hand box for minutes needs.
4. List all the digits the right-hand box for minutes needs.

Write these times in the way the digital clock shows them.
1. 11 o'clock
2. half past five
3. two o'clock
4. three forty-five
5. quarter to ten
6. twenty minutes past four o'clock

Here are six things Shaun has done in a school day. Make a table like the one below and fill in the activities. Then match each with the correct time. Shaun's school may have different times from yours.

Activity	Time done
1. Get out of bed	12:35
2. Have a wash and brush teeth	11:05
3. Have breakfast	8:50
4. Arrive at school	8:05
5. A geography lesson	7:20
6. Lunch	7:10

Look at the displays to decide whether these students are early or late.

1 Sam has to catch the train at five past six.

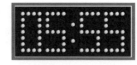

Has he missed the train? By how many minutes is he late or early?

2 Lessons start at 09.05. Kelly looks at her watch when she gets to school.

Was she early or late for class?

3 The film in the cinema begins at forty minutes past seven. Andrew looks at the clock when he arrives.

Was he early or too late to see the film?

4 Katherine's swimming lessons start at

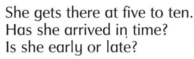

She gets there at five to ten. Has she arrived in time? Is she early or late?

5 Christine wants to watch 'Pop challenge' on television. It is now

Will she have missed the start of the programme?

Tuesday

BBC 1

3.30 **Children's TV** All your favourite cartoons and much more..............758996	**5.30** **Pop Challenge** Mike Land introduces all the hits from this week's top 40, featuring live performances from The Beautiful South and the latest videos...5384
4.25 **News Around** **The World** With Sebastian Parsons. Weather.................955618	**6.00** **Movie Highlights** Movie madness, exposing the latest cinema and video releases................522311
5.10 **B.M.X. Cross** **Country** Another edition of the topical bicycle program, in which Mark Young and Claire Wyatt keep an eye on the latest developments.............4256	**CHOICES** **Films**

Now look back at your work in this lesson.
- Do you have any digital clocks at home?
- What does the other type of clock look like? Do you know the name of this type of clock?

❸ Measuring time without the clock

We see the lightning before we hear the thunder.
You can count the seconds in-between in your head.
The longer the time the farther away the lightning.

Have a class discussion.
1. Why do people use egg-timers?
2. Why are there different size egg-timers?
3. Count in whisper while the teacher moves heel to toe across the classroom. Count steadily, without looking at the steps. Why are the counts different?
4. What is good about stopwatches?

In the box are six tasks for you to do. Choose a partner and both of you copy the table below.
1. Take turns. One of you does the task while the other watches and counts. Your partner must tell you to 'Ready, steady, go'. As you start, your partner needs to begin measuring the time you take.

	Task	Time
a	Read ten lines from a book in a whisper	
b	Throw a dice until you get a 6 three times	
c	Write your full name ten times	
d	Join ten unifix cubes (or beads) together	
e	Lace a trainer	

2. Find how long each task takes. Measure the time by counting evenly, or by using an egg-timer.

Task	Your time	Your partner's time
Reading		
Dice		
Writing		
Joining		
Lacing		

3. Record your results in the table.

C Look at the table you and your partner have completed.

1. List the activities in the order of the time it took you to do them.
2. Which activity was the fastest?
3. Which activity was the slowest?
4. Which activities do you think can be done faster with practice?
5. Which activities do you think cannot be done faster, even if you wanted to?

D The lighthouse beam goes round and round slowly, but regularly.
Imagine yourself holding a torch and turning around slowly.

1. Write down two actions that you can do in the time it takes the torch to shine in the same direction.
2. Estimate how many full turns the torch will make in one minute.

Now look back at your work in this lesson.
- Think of different ways to measure time.
- Can you count evenly? Is your counting the same as someone else's?

④ Ordering lengths

Which is the tallest building? Which is the shortest?
Which is the narrowest? Which is the widest?

Look at four friends in your class.
1. Write down their names in order of their height, tallest first.
2. Write their names in the reverse order, shortest first.
3. How can you be sure this is the right order?
4. Compare their hand spans. How do you know which is the widest?

Place four crayons (or pencils) on your desk and compare their lengths.
1. Sketch your arrangement.
2. Label the longest and the shortest crayons.
3. Label the narrowest and the widest.

Think about the lengths of these cars.

1. Put these cars in order of size, longest first.
2. How did you compare the lengths?
3. Which is nearest to the red car, the blue or the white?
4. Is there room for another car between car **a** and car **b**?

D

Look at the pictures below. Write them in order.

1 Write the names of the snakes in order of length, longest first.

Fred   Freda   Fareed

2 Now order the snakes by thickness.

3 Order the bottles in order of height.

a   b   c   d

4 Now order the bottles by width.

E

Measure the longer objects using the smaller ones as units.
Copy and complete the sentences using one of the phrases from the box.

> the same length   twice the length   three times the length
> many times the length

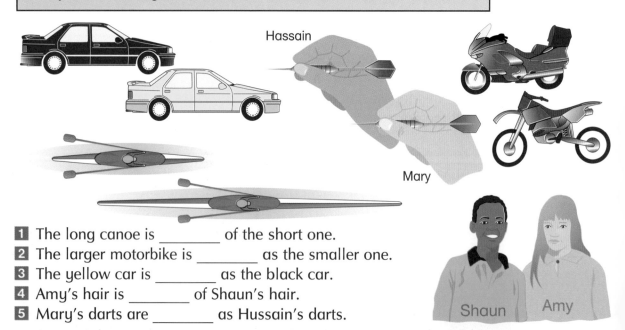

Hassain

Mary

Shaun   Amy

1 The long canoe is _____ of the short one.

2 The larger motorbike is _____ as the smaller one.

3 The yellow car is _____ as the black car.

4 Amy's hair is _____ of Shaun's hair.

5 Mary's darts are _____ as Hussain's darts.

Now look back at your work in this lesson.

- Is it easy to estimate width and length?
- Give different examples of how to order a group of things.

⑤ Comparing lengths

How many strides is it from the football goal to the spot for the goal kick?

 Have a class discussion.

1 What is the difference in length between a step and a stride in measuring distance?

2 Sometimes the height of ceilings in different classrooms is not the same. How can we tell this?

3 How can you find out if your classroom is really a square or whether any sides are longer than others?

Choose which measure is the best one to use.

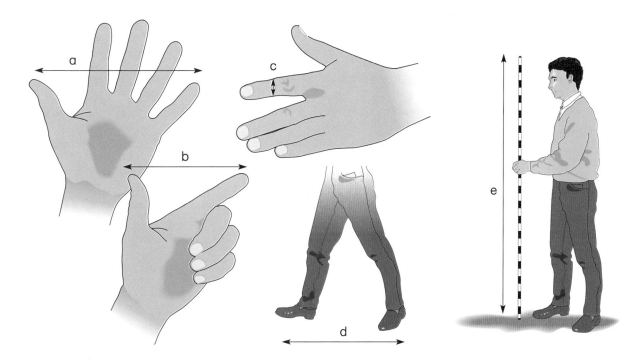

1 Which of two classrooms is biggest?
2 Which of two routes to go round the block is shorter in length?
3 Which of two desks is longer or higher?
4 Which of two swimming pools is deeper?
5 Which of two ceilings is higher?
6 Is the shape on a poster bigger or smaller than in a book?

Divide into groups of four.
1 Find out which of you has the smallest shoes without taking them off.
2 Who has the widest shoe?
3 Which of you can take the longest pace?
4 Who has the longest arm span?

Use your outstretched finger and thumb to measure the window.
1 How many times do you have to move your hand?
2 Now measure the teacher's desk in the same way.
3 Compare lengths. Which is the longest?

List these pictures in order of length. Begin with the longest first.

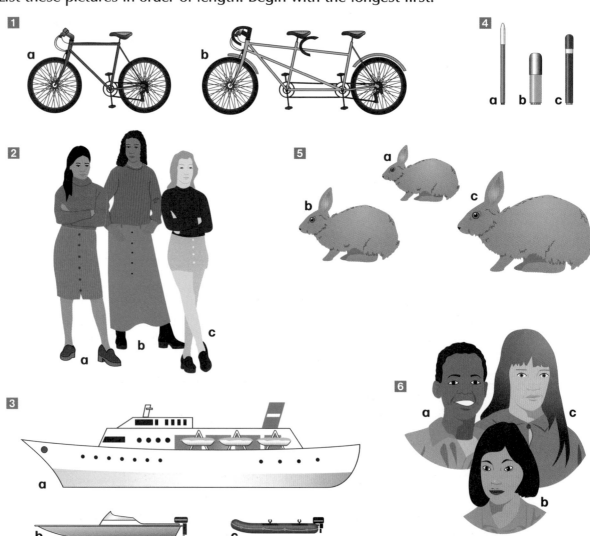

Now look back at your work in this lesson.
• Can you use different tools for measuring lengths?
• Can you measure approximately, using just your eye?

⑥ Measurement skills

Could you finish a stage of this race in the same time as these cyclists?

Using the following times, answer these questions.

| more than an hour | less than an hour |
| more than a minute | less than a minute |

1 How long does it takes to cycle 100 miles?
2 How long does it takes to bake a cake?
3 How long does it take to sew on a button?
4 How long does it take to boil an egg?
5 How long does it take to jump over a high jump bar?
6 How long does it take for an Olympic runner to run a 100 m race?

Look at the time shown on the school digital clock.

09:20

1 School started a quarter of an hour ago. What time was that?
2 It is two hours before the lunch break. What time will that be?
3 The lunch hour is really only 50 minutes. At what time does school start after lunch?
4 There will be afternoon games for one and a half hours. How many minutes is that?
5 How many minutes are left till ten o'clock?

Write down which you think it would take longer to do.
1 to eat an apple   or   to cross the street?
2 to play a whole CD   or   to fill a litre jug with water?
3 to wash a car   or   to travel thirty miles in a car?

Which is longer?
4 Twenty hours   or   one day?
5 Five full days   or   one week?
6 one month   or   three weeks?

D Compare the drawings.

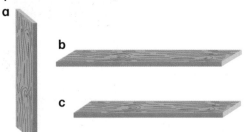

1 Which is the longest piece of wood?

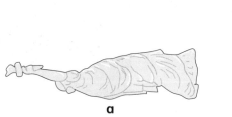

2 Which is the tallest statue?

3 Which of the animals is furthest away?
4 Which is the nearest?
5 In real life which animal will be the largest?
6 How did you decide that?

E Choose the best way to measure from the following methods.

| finger span | hand span | arm span | pace |

1 The length of a sports field
2 The width of a cupboard
3 The height of a coffee table
4 The width of a classroom
5 The length of a piece of paper
6 The distance between two trees

Now look back at your work in this lesson.
- How do you compare distance?
- How do you measure time?

Module A6

Handling data

❶ Recording what you see
Writing down what we know about people and things

❷ Sorting
Sorting things before deciding what to do with them

❸ Collecting and sorting
Recording things before sorting them into type or size or colour

❹ Ordering the information
Using information to put things in order

❺ Sorting before charting
Putting things in sets and then making bar charts

❻ Handling the observations
Recording, ordering and sorting require different skills

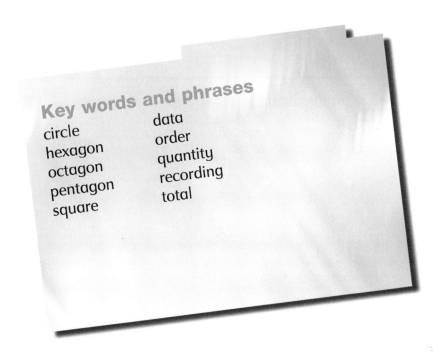

Key words and phrases

circle
hexagon
octagon
pentagon
square

data
order
quantity
recording
total

① **Recording what you see**

This policeman is collecting data on the car's speed. Is the driver going too fast?

Have a class discussion.
1 What does collecting data mean in the picture above?
2 What are other ways of collecting data?

Look carefully at what the people in the picture are wearing.

Ali   Brian   Carol   Farah   Ed   Dani

Harry

Gregor

1 How many people are wearing a hat?
2 Write all the names of those wearing hats.
3 How many are wearing a coat?
4 Write down their names.
5 What are the names of those in glasses?
6 Name a person that is wearing a coat but is not wearing a hat.
7 Which people are wearing a hat and glasses?
8 Who is wearing a hat, coat and glasses?

John has a dog. Brenda has a cat and a rabbit. Rakhee has a rabbit.

Brenda   Piers   Rakhee   Mike   John

1 Which children own a rabbit?
2 Which child owns a cat?
3 How many children own a dog?
4 How many children have two pets?
5 Who owns a rabbit and a dog but no cat?
6 How many dogs are there in the group?
7 Does anyone own a cat and a dog?
8 Does anyone own a cat and a rabbit?

Now do a survey.
1 Ask other people in your class which pets they own. Make up a list with two headings. Now fill in the names.

Name	Pet or pets

2 Count the number of each kind of pet and see which one has the largest total in your class. Organise the data in the table like this.

Pet	Number

Now look back at your work in this lesson.
- Did you know that making a list is collecting data?
- Give two ways you can arrange data.

② Sorting

What types of hat can you see in this picture, and how many of each?

Here is a collection of circles with different patterns.

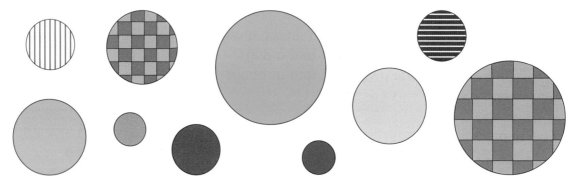

1 How many circles have a square pattern on them?
2 How many have stripes?
3 How many circles are left?
4 What sort of pattern do they have?

Here are some shoes.

1 How many shoes can you see?
2 How many pairs can you make?
3 Are there any shoes left over? If so how many?

In the picture are three groups of vehicles.

1 Why have the vehicles been put into these groups?
2 Which group has the most?
3 Which group has the least?

Look at the vehicles in exercise C again.
1 Can you find another way to sort them into three groups using a different rule?
2 Do a rough drawing of the new groups.

Leanne dropped a box of paper clips and rubber bands.

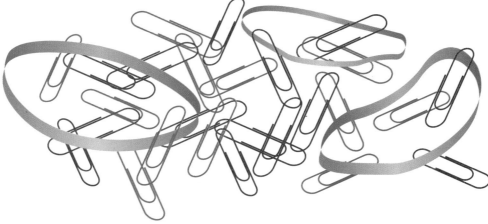

1 If Leanne sorted them into two piles how many would there be in each?
2 If she decided to sort them into three piles how many would there be in each?

Now look back at your work in this lesson.
• Think of two ways to group things.
• Can you think of things that you sort in your own home?

③ Collecting and sorting

Daily jobs often involve collecting and sorting.

Have a class discussion.

1 Why does the florist sort the plants out in groups?

2 In the picture, are there more sorted or unsorted pots?

Here are some pot plants that need to be arranged on a shelf in the florist's shop.

1 Can you think of a way to arrange them so they are in attractive groups?

2 Which plants would go in each group? Do a quick drawing of your idea.

3 What is an alternative way to arrange them?

4 Arrange the plants to fit your new idea.

Here is some cutlery for your table.

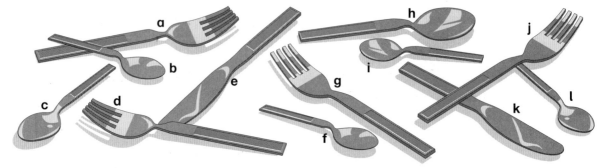

1 Choose five items that go together from this collection.

2 What makes them go together?

The china shop next door has had a new delivery of coffee mugs.

1. Count how many colours the mugs come in.
2. Make a list of the different designs which are on the mugs.
3. If you were arranging the mugs in a display, how would you place them in groups on a shelf?
4. Which mugs would you put in each group?
5. The owner of the shop does not like your arrangement! How else could you group the mugs?

Jemma found a box of shapes.

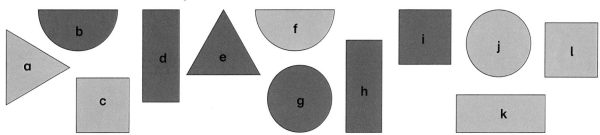

1. Sort these shapes into two sets.
2. Select six shapes that have something in common.
3. Write down what is common to your selection.

Which supermarket does your family use? Do you think that the families of everyone in your class use the same one?
1. Make a list of as many supermarkets in your area that you can think of.
2. Work with one or two friends. Find out from all the people in your class which is their favourite supermarket and record it on your list.
3. Think of a way to improve your record. Will it be necessary to include names on your list?

Now look back at your work in this lesson.
- Can you think of three different ways to sort things into groups?
- Have you learnt any new words during this lesson?

④ Ordering the information

Why do supermarkets arrange their products in different ways?

 Look at the following tins.

1 How many tins of beans are there?
2 How many tins of peas can you see?
3 What is in the other tins?
4 How many of these are on the shelf?

 Look again at the picture of tins.
1 Are there more tins of beans or more tins of peas?
2 Which kind of tinned vegetable does the store have the least of?
3 Put the three kinds of vegetable in order starting with the largest quantity.

C

Each week Mr Patel orders seven cartons of Corn Flakes, five cartons of Rice Krispies and three cartons of Weetabix for his store.

1. Which cereal do you think he sells the most of?
2. Do more customers buy Weetabix or Rice Krispies each week?
3. Put the three kinds of cereal in order of popularity starting with the least popular.

D

Mrs McGregor buys her fresh vegetables at Mr Patel's store. Each week she has seven kilograms of potatoes, three kilograms of carrots, one kilogram of onions and four kilograms of green vegetables.

1. Which kind of vegetable does Mrs McGregor's family eat the most of?
2. Do they eat more carrots or more green vegetables?
3. If Mrs McGregor had to shop for two weeks how many kilograms of each vegetable would she have to buy?
4. Put the vegetables in order of the amount used each week starting with the greatest.

E

Here is a bar graph that shows how many cases of soft drinks Mr Patel sells in a month.

1. Which is the most popular drink?
2. Does he sell more Lemonade or more Orangeade?
3. Which drink is twice as popular as Sprite?
4. Write the drinks in order of popularity.

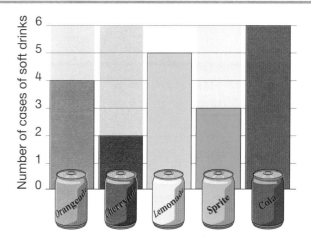

Now look back at your work in this lesson.
- Can you sort things into groups and then make a bar chart of the data?
- Do you think arranging food in supermarkets is useful?

⑤ Sorting before charting

It's easy to lose pieces of a board game. When you want to play you must check first that all the pieces are there. So you start by sorting the bits.

Mrs Miller has an old box of shapes in her cupboard. There should be 12 of each shape, but some of them are missing. There is only one set that is complete.

1 Which one is complete?
2 Which sets of shapes have two missing?
3 Which shape has she lost the most of?
4 Arrange the shapes in order of the amounts that are still left, starting with the most.

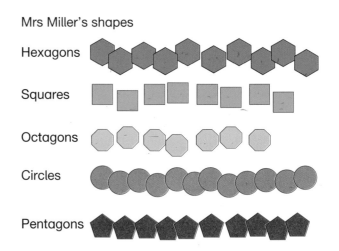

Mrs Miller's shapes

Hexagons

Squares

Octagons

Circles

Pentagons

Here is a bar chart which shows the number of hours of sunshine during six days last June.

1 Which was the cloudiest day?
2 If you wanted to spend a day on the beach which day would have been the best?
3 Two days had the same amount of sun. Which were they?
4 Write down the days in order starting with the sunniest.
5 Re-draw the bar chart in this order.

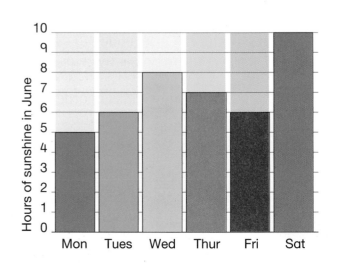

Jo made a table for the temperatures she recorded in the mornings and afternoons last week. Here are her readings in degrees Centigrade.

	Morning / °C	Afternoon / °C
Monday	15	21
Tuesday	17	24
Wednesday	16	25
Thursday	20	21
Friday	22	24

1 Work out the rise in temperature for each day.
2 Which day had the greatest rise in temperature?
3 On which day did the temperature rise by only 1°C?
4 Write the days in order starting with the day with the greatest rise and ending with the day that had the smallest change.

Bet and Ali both drew a bar chart to show the number of pets that their friends have.
Sally is re-arranging one of the pet bar charts in order of popularity. She has not labelled her axes yet.

Ali's pet chart

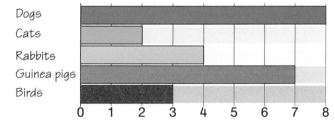

Bet's pet chart

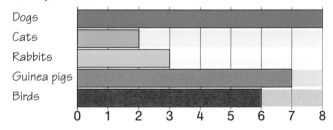

Sally's pet chart

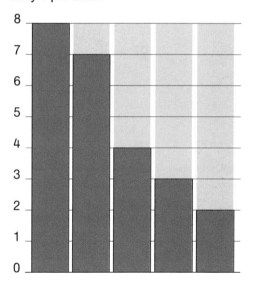

1 Whose bar chart is Sally re-arranging?
2 List the animals in the same order that Sally has shown them and say how many of each there are.

Now look back at your work in this lesson.
- How can bar charts of weather during different months be useful?
- What would be a different way of sorting pets?

⑥ Handling the observations

What differences are there between these buildings?

Look at these buildings.

1 How many shops are in the picture?
2 Write down the names of the shops and what kind of items they sell.
3 Make another list of the shops in order of size starting with the smallest.

Look at the hotels in the picture.

1 How many of the buildings are hotels?

2 The Grand Hotel has 50 bedrooms, the Burlington Hotel has 10 less than the Grand and the Beach Hotel has 5 more than the Burlington. The Sea View has 15 bedrooms and the Mermaid has 10 bedrooms. Which is the largest hotel?

3 If all the hotels are full in August, which one will cook the most food for a week?

4 Copy the axes below and then draw a bar chart of the number of bedrooms in each hotel. Put the hotels in order of the number of bedrooms, starting with the most.

60 _____

50 _____

40 _____

30 _____

20 _____

10 _____

0 _____

Number of rooms

Hotels

C Where do people live while on holidays? Use the blackboard when answering these questions.

1 With your teacher's help, make a list like this one of the different kinds of accommodation that people may spend their holidays in.

Holiday	Name
At home	
Hotel	
Log cabin	
Cruise	

2 Now each person writes their name against any accommodation they have used in any of their last three holidays (or trips). If anyone thinks of places not listed then add them to the list.

3 Count the number of people in each type.

4 Copy the list in order of popularity, and write in the number of people that have used the accommodation.

5 Draw a bar chart to show the number of people in your class that stayed in each kind of holiday accommodation, starting with the least popular.

D Some people enjoy boating holidays. Think about how these boats are powered.

1 Sort this collection into three sets.

2 Draw a bar chart of your data.

Now look back at your work in this lesson.
* Can you make groups of almost anything?
* How could a bar chart provide useful information to the cooks in your school?

Module **A**7

Number and measurement

❶ Counting accurately

Practising not missing anything and not counting anything twice

❷ Symbols for missing numbers

Finding the number that a symbol represents from a pattern or a sum

❸ Using number scales

Finding the number from the position of a mark near other parts of a scale

❹ Three-digit numbers

Reading and writing three-digit numbers means knowing which digits are for the hundreds, which for the tens and which for the units

❺ Up and down between 100 and 1000

Counting up or down can be done in a pattern starting from any number, and crossing the 100s mark

❻ Number skills

Reading scales, accurate counting, and finding missing numbers are important when working with numbers

Key words and phrases

calculate
code
highest and lowest
maximum
measure
number scale
weigh

calculator
digit
length
millimetre
order
score
sum

① Counting accurately

How long would it take to sew on so many pearls?

Use small circles to draw some of the letters and shapes made in pearls. Then count the small circles in each shape.

1. The letter **P**
2. The horseshoe shape
3. The sun shape
4. The triangle on the Pearly King's arm

Look at this bus queue.

1. How many men are there in the queue?
2. How many women are there?
3. How many boys are there?
4. How many girls are there?
5. The bus takes a maximum of 32 people. Will all the people in the queue get on?

Look at the chess board. Count the squares.

1 How many black squares are there?
2 How many white squares?
3 How many squares altogether?

Look at these stamps.

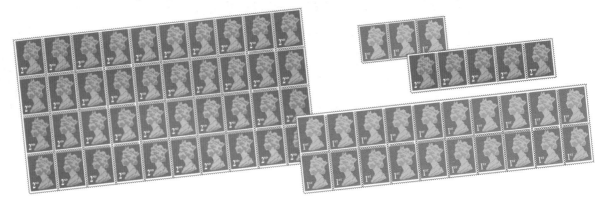

1 How many first class stamps are there?
2 How many stamps altogether?

Look at these windows and count the number of small window panes.

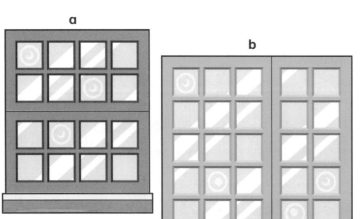
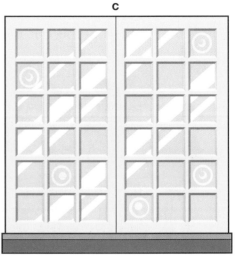

1 How many window panes are there in window **a**?
2 How many panes are there in window **b**?
3 How many panes are there in window **c**?
4 Altogether there are _____ window panes.

Answer these questions.

1 Linda has a pack of 12 felt-tipped pens. John has lent her some more. How many pens has she altogether?

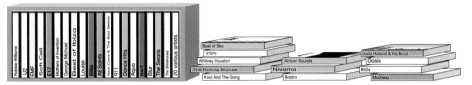

2 Bhavin can't fit all his CDs in his rack. The rack holds 20 CDs. How many CDs has he altogether?

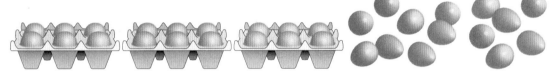

3 Vicky is working on a farm. So far she has filled three boxes with eggs. How many eggs does she have to pack altogether?

4 Winston has bought a packet of 36 fun-size chocolate bars. His mum has bought him some more. How many chocolate bars has he got altogether?

5 Simon rolls three dice. What his total score?

6 Fatima rolls three dice. What is her total score?

Now look back at your work in this lesson.
- Sometimes estimating is not precise enough. Can you count accurately?
- Can you count in parts and then add the parts together to reach a total?

② Symbols for missing numbers

Can you understand what is being said here?

A

What are the numbers that are hidden in these sums?

1 $4 + \text{✏} = 8$

2 $4 + \text{✏} = 8$

3 $3 + \text{✏} = 10$

4 $\text{✏} + 5 = 10$

5 $7 + \text{✏} = 15$

6 $12 + \text{✏} = 20$

7 $10 + 6 = \text{✏}$

8 $\text{✏} + 8 = 17$

B

What numbers should go in these boxes? Use a calculator.

1 $5 \times ? = 15$

2 $7 \times ? = 21$

3 $? \times 8 = 64$

4 $4 \times ? = 40$

5 $5 \times ? = 25$

6 $6 \times ? = 66$

C

Each red circle represents a coin. What should the coin be in each case?

1 $3 \times \bullet = 6p$

2 $4 \times \bullet = 40p$

3 $5 \times \bullet = 5p$

4 $\bullet + \bullet = £1$

5 $6 \times \bullet = 30p$

6 $3 \times \bullet = 60p$

D

Spot the pattern of the numbers to find the numbers in the envelopes.

1 2, 4, 6, ✉, 10, 12

2 3, 6, 9, 12, ✉, 18

3 5, 10, 15, ✉, 25

4 3, 6, ✉, 24, 48

5 1, 4, 7, ✉, 13, 16

6 12, 10, 8, ✉, 4

The enemy has used this code. Break the code!

D = 3 × 2	G = 10 − 5
E = 12 − 4	T = 6 + 3
L = 5 ÷ 5	S = 10 − 7
N = 12 ÷ 3	O = 4 + 3

1 Read this message:
6 7   4 7 9   5 7   9 7   1 8 8 6 3

2 What does this message say?
5 8 9   9 7   1 7 4 6 7 4   3 7 7 4

3 Think of a word using these letters. Write it in code and give it to someone to try to read. Take turns.

Jo, Bob, Tom, Ann, Lin and Roy go to a rock concert. Look at their tickets.

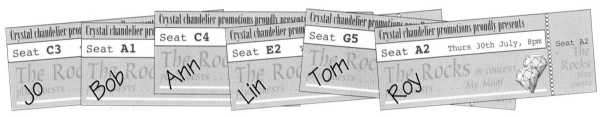

Copy this grid and fill in their names in the correct cells.

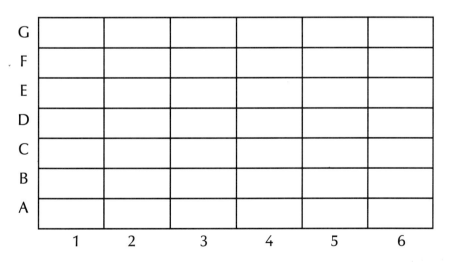

Now look back at your work in this lesson.
- Can you look at patterns to find a missing number?
- Make up a secret code of your own.

③ Using number scales

Many churches appeal for extra funding for special projects such as repairs or new furniture. Do you know of other appeals for cash made by charities?

In this picture, how much money has been raised so far? Do you think the church is half-way to reaching the target?

Michael and his friends are also collecting for charity. How much has each of them collected?

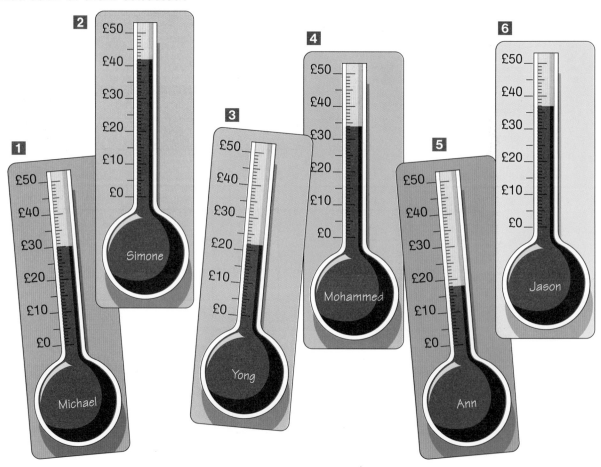

Write down the exact speed of each car.

These thermometers show the temperatures in six capital cities at midday on one summer day.
Write down the temperature for each city.

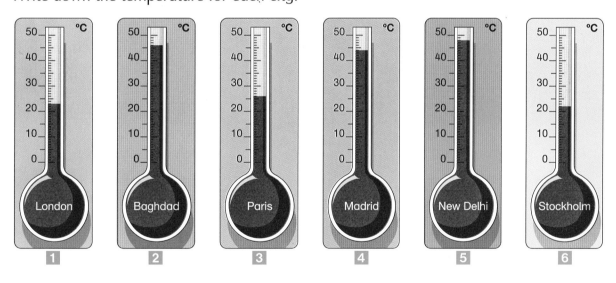

London — 1 Baghdad — 2 Paris — 3 Madrid — 4 New Delhi — 5 Stockholm — 6

Measure these lines carefully with a ruler. Write down the lengths to the nearest millimetre.

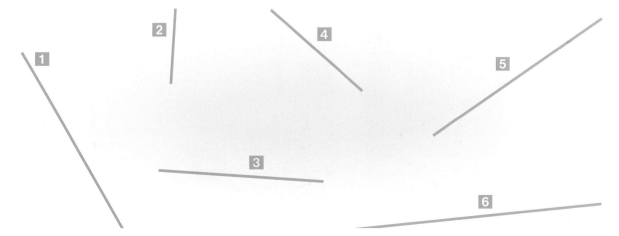

E

Tina works in a delicatessen. She is weighing cheese to the nearest ten grams. Write in the weights of each portion of cheese by checking the scales.

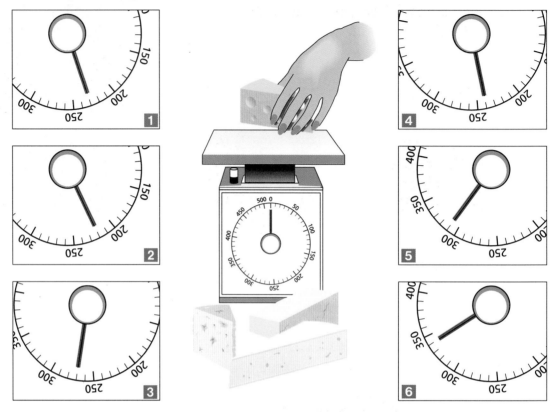

F

Winston and his friends have been counting their CDs. They record each five like this: 卌. How many do each of them have?

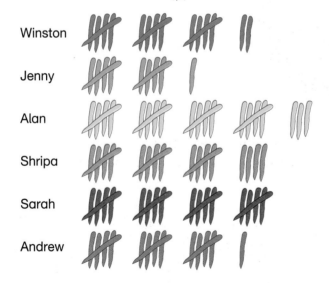

Winston

Jenny

Alan

Shripa

Sarah

Andrew

Now look back at your work in this lesson.
- Can you read different amounts from number scales?
- What are the different things number scales can show?

Three-digit numbers

Why do you think such large numbers are necessary in international athletic games? Can you read all the numbers in the picture?

A Carefully copy these numbers with the largest first.

572 Croydon

Chi 231

Hymn
381
621
127

718

Leung 405

B Hanif and his friends are playing darts. Add ten to each and write down their scores.

Hanif 243
Debbie 256
Jane 231
Winston 220
Fatima 199
Phillip 178

C Jane and some of her friends live in the same block of flats. Here are their flat numbers. The first digit shows which floor the flat is on.

Sue 304
Shripa 315
Mark 327
Jane 103
Norbert 233
Aksar 223

1 Write the numbers of the flats on the third floor.

Fatima and her friends all catch different buses to school. Here are their bus numbers. The first digit of the bus number indicates the garage number from which it starts.

Fatima

Wayne

Winston

Melissa

Sarfraz

Joanne

1 Write the numbers of the buses which start from the same garage together. You should have three groups of numbers.

2 It is possible to read the bus numbers 245 as 'two four five' instead of 'two hundred and forty-five'. Why is that?

Sarah is looking at prices in a sale. She needs to make a list of them for her mum and dad.

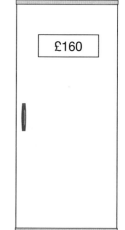

1 Write Sarah's list.

2 Write in words the price of the most expensive item.

3 Write in words the price of the cheapest item.

Now look back at your work in this lesson.
* Can you write numbers in words?
* How are three-digit amounts of money different from three-digit flat numbers?

⑤ Up and down between 100 and 1000

Every 100 metres there are resting places to give climbers a break. Where do you think the next two benches will be?

Put these numbers in order starting with the lowest and finishing with the highest.

1 126   122   129   128
2 268   251   275   293
3 676   642   609   681
4 156   435   320   104
5 728   615   838   421

For an April Fool's joke, Rachel changed the order of the loose pages of her friends' folders. Now put them back into their correct order.

1 Susan's page numbers
   125 124 128 127 126 123
2 Afsar's page numbers
   143 140 142 144 141 139
3 Rushna's page numbers
   166 164 167 168 163 165
4 Simon's page numbers
   189 191 188 192 190 187
5 Jack's page numbers
   119 117 120 116 121 118

Sandra and her friends play a computer game. Here are their scores after half an hour.

NAME	SCORE
John	184
Fahema	205
Sandra	197
Hussain	226
Linda	182
Altab	179

1 Find the winner and then put the rest in order.

A ticket machine goes faulty and issues tickets out of order. Put them back in order.

1	558	563	561	560	559	562
2	873	870	875	872	874	871
3	665	664	667	663	666	662
4	202	199	200	203	198	201
5	98	100	97	101	96	99

Six friends live in the same block of flats. The flats are numbered in order, and all of the friends have neighbours on either side.

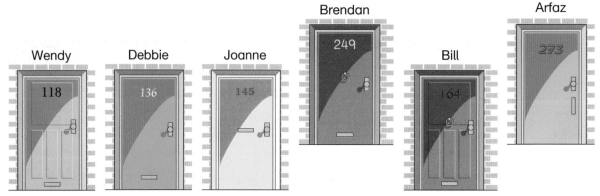

1 Write down the numbers of the flats.
2 Write down the numbers of the neighbours on both sides.

Brian's teacher has a set of cards numbered 1–1000 but they are out of order and some are missing. She gives a group of his friends a set of cards to put in order and asks them to write down the numbers of missing cards.

Write the correct order and the missing cards for each of these sets.

1 Paul – 120s
   125 124 120 128 127 123 122 129
2 Sarah – 140s
   145 148 149 140 142 147 146 144
3 Hanif – 150s
   152 157 159 153 150 156 151 155
4 Alan – 180s
   187 189 180 183 181 188 185 186
5 Teresa – 190s
   196 198 193 190 194 192 195 197

Now look back at your work in this lesson.
• Can you put three-digit numbers in order?
• What do you start with when you are ordering large numbers?

⑥ Number skills

There are many different games that use dominoes.
Each game has different rules.

In this game of dominoes the player scores the number of dots between the previous six and the new six they place.

What has each player scored? You can either count the number of dots between the sixes or just double the dots in the middle domino.

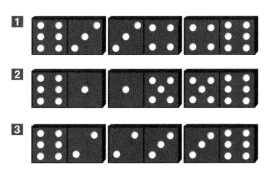

The letters used in this code are D, G, K, O, R and W.
Crack this code using the answers to these sums.

D = 12 − 5	O = 6 ÷ 3
G = 5 + 3	R = 12 − 8
K = 9 ÷ 9	W = 12 ÷ 2

1 8 2 2 7 6 2 4 1

Copy the following ten numbers on to two sets of card.
Now play a card game with a friend.

561 854 165 845 651 516 501 156 105 615

1 You both take a set of cards and shuffle them. Place each set face down and turn over the top card at the same time.

2 The one who turns over the biggest number takes both the cards and puts them in a separate pile.

3 The winner is the person who has the most cards in the separate pile. Play to the best of three games. If the numbers are the same, push them aside and do not count them.

Write down the exact speed of these cars.

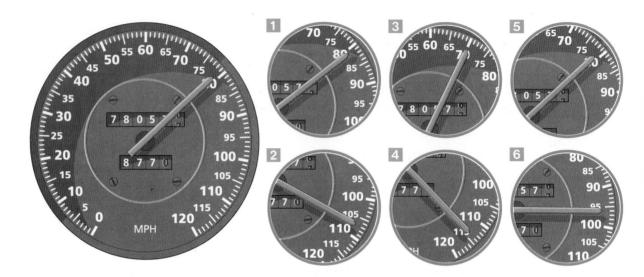

Jason has started work as a postman. Help him put his letters
in order of the number of the houses. Start from the lowest number.

1 Rupert Street
   123   57   218   5   149   56
2 St Mary's Avenue
   182   198   18   74   5   17
3 John Street
   157   98   17   162   84   161
4 Charlotte Road
   17   184   23   2   162   14
5 Clifford Road
   82   17   127   59   68   3
6 Matilda Close
   44   15   142   33   121   100

Copy and fill in the missing numbers.

1 81,   83,   ___,   87,   89,   ___
2 121,   124,   127,   ___,   133,   ___
3 450,   455,   ___,   465,   ___,   475
4 11,   22,   ___,   44,   55,   ___
5 830,   840,   ___,   ___,   870,   880
6 140,   138,   ___,   134,   132,   ___

Now look back at your work in this lesson.
• Can you fill in missing three-digit numbers in patterns?
• Make a code for your friend to crack!

Module A8

Shape and space

1 **Fitting rectangles together**

Fitting rectangular shapes together in different ways,
all of which include lining up the straight edges.
Rectangular boxes are stacked in similar ways

2 **Tiling**

Fitting flat shapes together with no gaps, for example
triangles and hexagons of the same size

3 **Line maps**

Understanding that railway maps and bus maps are
made with lines that branch and cross each other with
stations following each other on the lines

4 **Reading maps**

Knowing where you are and which way you are facing is
important in reading street maps as well as being careful
with your left and right turns, and when to turn next...

5 **Describing routes**

Describing buildings and parks on the way can make your
map directions easier

6 **Map skills**

Combining skills is important when map reading. Often
maps have extra signs that give more information as well
as lines and shapes

Key words and phrases

centre	direction	branch and fork
curved	fitting	bus map
go from and go to	left and right turns	hexagon
route	lining up	line map
straight edge	route	railway map
symbols	tiling	stack

① Fitting rectangles together

In the game 'Jenga' it is easy to stack up the pieces because of their shape. The pieces fit together very well... until they topple!

Here is the deck of a ferry. The rectangles are parking bays for cars.

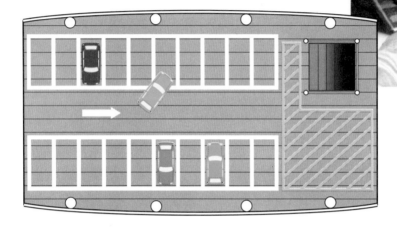

1 Could the parking bays be drawn another way?

2 Collect some tiles from your teacher and imagine they are the bays. Try different ways of fitting the bays together, making sure the straight edges touch each other.

Three patterns have been started with the fridge magnets.

a
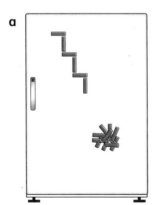

b
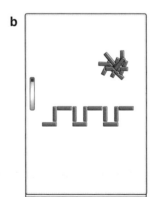

c

1 Copy these patterns and then continue each pattern using the spare magnets. The magnets should fit with the others and not leave gaps.

Ryan is putting down block pavings on his drive. His blocks have a square face and are in two colours. He arranges them in a pattern.

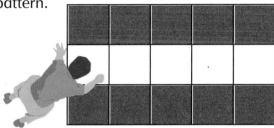

His son says that looks boring.

1 Can you create a more interesting look for the drive? Use the five white and ten red tiles only.

In a fish market the fishermen arrange their crates of fish so that there is room for buyers to walk around.

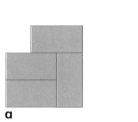
a

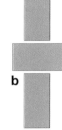
b

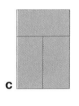
c

d

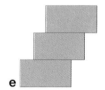
e

1 If the crates are arranged like this how should the next boat put its two crates? Use tracing paper to copy the arrangment and add two extra crates for each arrangement.

On a school trip to Hampton Court, Tom and Lynne saw these different patterns on the brick walls.

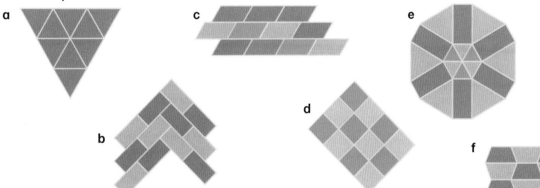

1 Which of the patterns are made up of rectangles fitted together?

Now look back at your work in this lesson.
• Try making your own pattern of rectangles.
• Choose another shape and try to make a pattern with it.

② Tiling

In Tetris you have to move the pieces so that they make up solid rows. Some pieces fit easily, others need turning over as well as around to slot in.

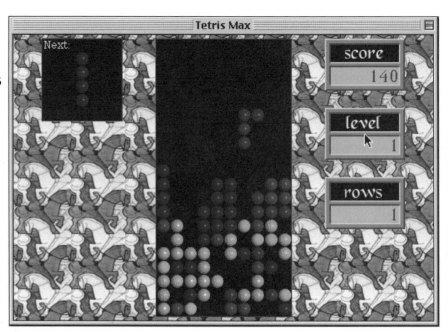

The Bank of England is making presentation packs for special coins. The coins are held in velvet pieces.

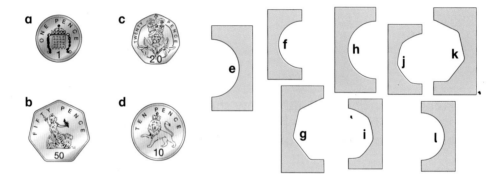

1 Which holding pieces will fit each coin? Each of the four coins must have two holding pieces.

2 Why are the holding pieces not the same?

From this selection Elaine must choose tiles for her floor.

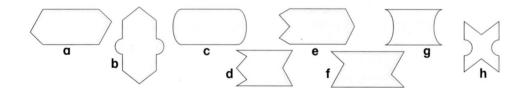

1 She wants two different tiles which will fit together and cover the floor in all directions. Which should she choose?

2 Use tracing paper to show how the two different tiles fit each other without gaps.

Saria blows these glass vases. To send them through the post, they are placed on a bed of cotton wool and packed tightly with a card frame which fits the shape of the vase.

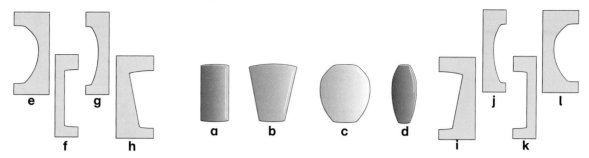

1. Which two card shapes fit the vases shown?
2. Think about how you found the two cards. Which card did you look at first?
3. In which order did you look at the other cards?

The packing of chocolate eggs for Easter is getting harder. Everyone wants different shaped eggs! These frames come in four pieces.

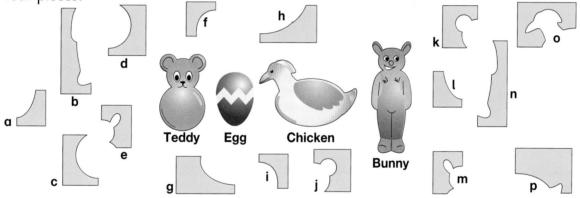

1. Which four pieces of card will be needed to fit these eggs?

Play this game with a partner. Both players take two A4 cards of the same colour and cut each card into three different shaped pieces. Jumble all the pieces in the middle.

1. Take two dice and roll one each. Whoever gets the highest score can choose a piece of card.
2. The first to make a complete card wins.
3. If you roll a 6 you can take a piece from the other player!

Now look back at your work in this lesson.
- Can you think of any shapes which would fit together like tiles, other than a square or rectangle?
- Which are easier to fit together – pieces with curved edges or pieces with angles?

③ Line maps

This is the most successful map in London. Millions of people use it every day!

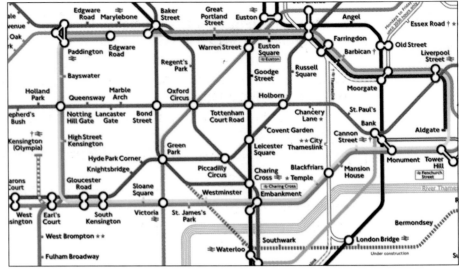

A

Look at this map of a theme park. Imagine you start from the Burger Bar.

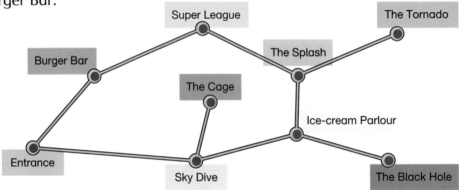

1 Which rides would you pass if you went to the Tornado?

B

Follow these journeys around the theme park in exercise **A** using the map and say where they began and ended. Copy and complete the sentences.

1 I started at the _____ and walked past the Entrance and the Sky Dive and had a ride on the _____.
2 I started at the _____ and walked past the Super League and the Splash and had a ride on the _____.
3 I started at the _____ and walked past the Entrance, the Burger Bar and the Super League and had a ride on the _____.
4 I started at the _____ and walked past the Sky Dive, the Ice Cream Parlour, the Splash and the Super League and bought something at the _____.
5 I started at the _____ and walked past the Ice Cream Parlour, the Splash and the Super League and bought something at the _____.
6 I started at the _____ and walked past the Burger Bar, the Entrance and the Sky Dive and had a ride on the _____.

Say which rides you would pass as you walk around the theme park. Copy and complete the sentences.

1 What would you pass if you started from the Burger Bar and went to the Black Hole?

2 What would you pass if you started from the Cage and went to the Tornado?

3 What would you pass if you started from the Tornado and went to the Black Hole?

4 What would you pass if you started from the Burger Bar and went to the Cage?

5 What would you pass if you started from the Entrance and went to the Black Hole?

This map is from a computer game. To survive you must take the shortest route.

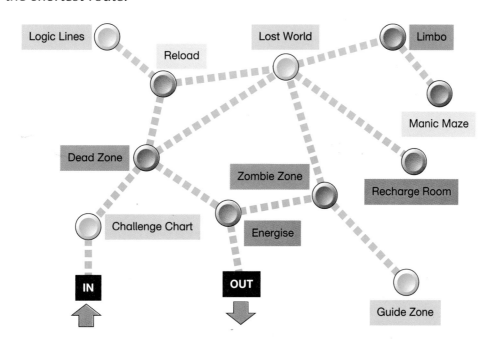

1 Which zones have you travelled through if you start at Guide Zone and end at Manic Maze?

2 Is this the shortest route? Energise – Dead Zone – Reload – Lost World

3 Which zones have you travelled through if you start at Guide Zone and end at Logic Lines?

4 Which zones have you travelled through if you start at Zombie Zone and end at In?

5 Which zones have you travelled through if you start at Manic Maze and end at Challenge Chart?

6 Which zones have you travelled through if you start at In and end at Guide Zone?

7 Which zones have you travelled through if you start at Logic Lines and end at Energise?

Are these the shortest routes from one to the other? If not, which route is?

1 Manic Maze – Limbo – Lost World – Reload – Dead Zone – Energise – Out

2 Recharge Room – Lost World – Zombie Zone – Energise – Out

3 Logic Lines – Reload – Dead Zone – Energise – Zombie Zone – Guide Zone

4 In – Challenge Chart – Dead Zone – Reload – Lost World – Limbo

5 In – Challenge Chart – Dead Zone – Energise – Zombie Zone – Guide Zone

Here is a map of two floors of a school. Notice that the staircase shown on the ground floor is the same staircase shown on the first floor.

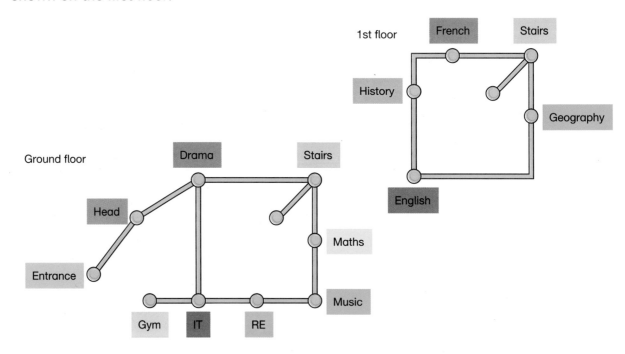

1 Describe my route if I arrive in the Entrance and must get to Geography.

2 Describe my route if I leave my Maths lesson and go to English.

3 Which lesson did I leave if I pass Music, Maths and French on my way to History?

4 You are given a message by the headteacher. You must take it to every room. Describe your route.

Now look back at your work in this lesson.
- Can you use a map to find your way around?
- Draw a map of the route from your house to the nearest shop.

④ Reading maps

The skill of reading maps takes a lot of practice. You must find where you are on the map and which way you are facing.

 Here is a map of Middleton in Suffolk.

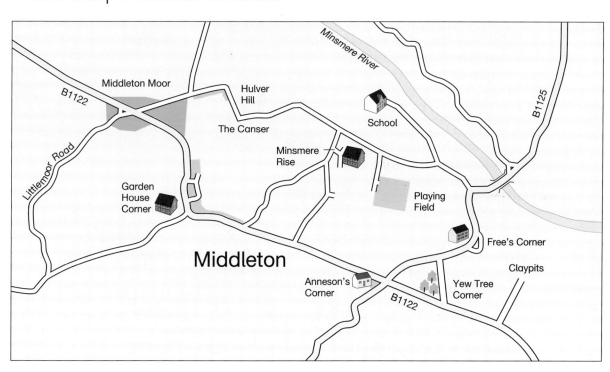

1 Describe a route which would take you from Free's Corner to Minsmere Rise.

2 Describe a route which would take you from Hulver Hill to Anneson's Corner.

3 Daniel is at the playing field. Describe his route to get to his home in Littlemoor Road.

4 Ishbel is at the school. Describe her route to get to her home in Garden House Corner.

5 Callum leaves the playing field and walks to meet Ishbel from school. What route does he take?

6 Daniel wants to meet up with Ishbel and Callum on their way home. Where should they wait for each other?

7 Emily and Sarah each choose a different route from Minsmere Rise to Claypits. Describe the two routes.

Look at this map of Wimpole Hall.

1 If Isaac stands at the Folly looking towards the Hall is Oddy Doddy Lane to his right or his left?

2 If Katie stands on the path between the lakes looking towards the farm is the Folly on her right or her left?

3 If Melanie stands in the gardens with her back to the Hall will the farm be to her right or her left?

4 If Meena walks along the straight track marked as West Avenue towards the Hall will the lakes be on her right or her left?

5 Where do you think Halim is if he has Oddy Doddy Lane behind him, the lakes slightly to his right and the Hall slightly to his left?

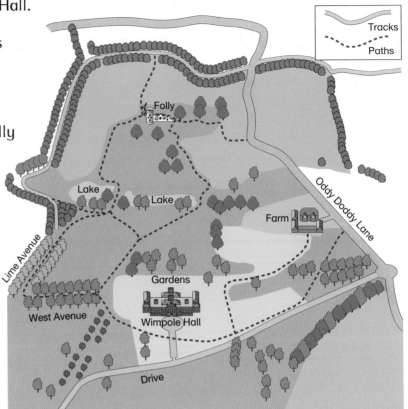

Tracks

Paths

Folly

Lake

Lake

Farm

Lime Avenue

Oddy Doddy Lane

Gardens

West Avenue

Wimpole Hall

Drive

Follow the routes on the map of Wimpole Hall to find the answer.

1 Where would David be after walking this route?
"I left the farm on a curved track and walked past the front of the Hall. I took the next turn on my right and stopped at a fork in the path for my lunch. I had a lovely view!"

2 Sarah left the farm on the same route as David but she turned down the drive to visit the Hall. As she leaves the Hall what route should she take to meet David for lunch?

3 After lunch they both take the left fork and walk between the two lakes and round a curved track to the Folly. They want to return to the farm along Oddy Doddy Lane. Describe their route.

4 Saida is at the junction of West Avenue and Lime Avenue. She wants to visit the Folly but not to walk between the lakes. Describe her route.

Now look back at your work in this lesson.
• Can you follow a route on a map?
• Do you have a map of where you live? Is it easy for newcomers to get lost?

⑤ Describing routes

Nowadays, computers can tell you the best route to take.

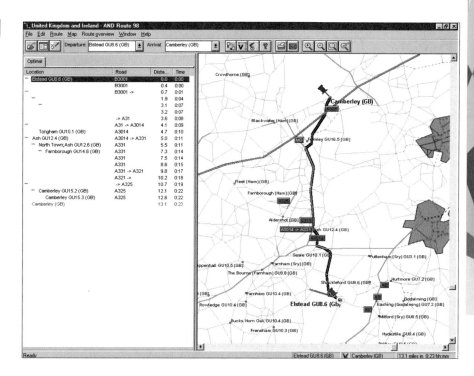

Look at this map of Alphabet Park.

1 Which signs on the park are not square?

2 Which are squares?

3 How many tracks are curved? Where do they run from and to?

4 How many tracks are straight? Where do they run from and to?

5 Start from Fox Hole taking the curved track. At the next junction take the left track. At the next junction, which is a T-junction, take a left turn. Where are you? Underline the third letter of the second word.

6 Make up similar instructions to take you to a place where you can underline a letter **e**.

Four of these shapes fit together to form one rectangle.

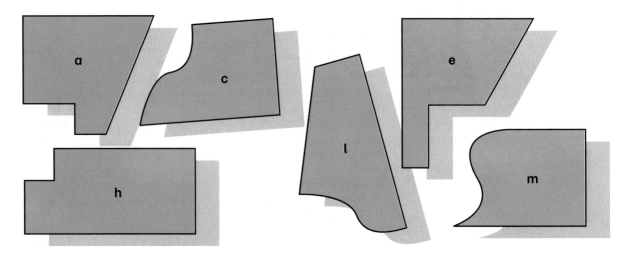

1. Trace the six shapes on tracing paper.
2. Cut the pieces out with scissors.
3. Find the four pieces that make a rectangle and write their letters.
4. Out of the shapes which you used in question 3, which ones had curved sides? Write down their letters – you will need them for exercise E.

Copy these sections of a map on to tracing paper. The map is a square – fit your pieces of tracing paper together to form a square map.

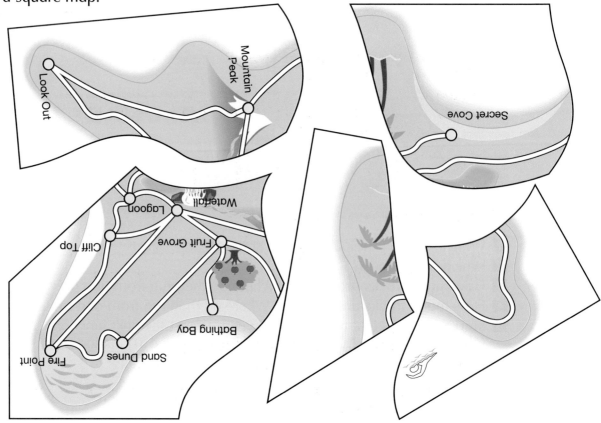

Use the map you have made to follow these instructions.

1 Start from Secret Cove. At the first junction take the second left. At the junction of five tracks take the first left and walk along this straight track.

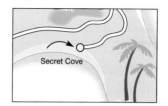

Where are you? Write the first letter of the second word.

2 Leave the Sand Dunes along the straight track. At the first junction turn left. When you reach the next junction turn sharp right. Continue along this straight track.

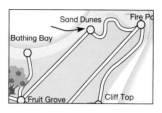

Where are you? Write down the second letter of the first word.

3 Leave Fire Point on the middle track. At the next junction take a right turn.

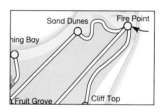

Where are you? Write down the last letter of the first word.

4 Start from Cliff Top taking the middle track. At the next track junction take the route which bears to the right but not sharp right. Do the same again at the next junction.

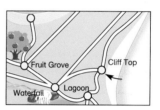

Where are you? Write down the fifth letter of the first word.

You now have two letters from exercise B and four from exercise D. You need two more.

1 Put the six letters together and guess the two missing letters. Arrange them so that they will tell you the place on the island map where the treasure is buried.

2 What would be your idea of treasure?

3 Use a route around Alphabet Park (see the map in exercise A) to give clues to spell out where your treasure is hidden.

4 Give the instructions to your partner to unravel your treasure mystery.

Now look back at your work in this lesson.
- Can you draw a map from your house to your school?
- Have you used maps to find your way to somewhere new? Do you think you could?

⑥ Map skills

A picture taken from an aeroplane seems more realistic than a map of the same area. But it does not give you as much information. What can a map tell you that a picture can't?

 Look at this map of a city centre. There are some drawings and symbols which you need to recognise.

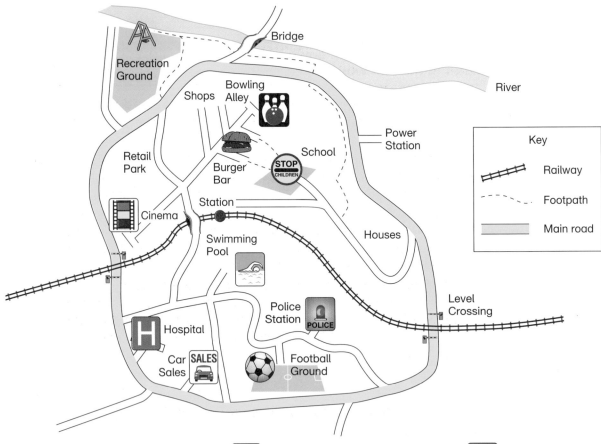

1 What does this symbol show?   **2** What does this show? **H**

3 A passenger on a train sees the cinema on the left. On which side will the swimming pool be?

4 Follow Stephen's moves to see where he ends this journey. He leaves the swimming pool. At the crossroads he turns right. When he gets to the ring road he turns right again and continues around this curving road. He goes down the next entrance on his left, after the railway bridge.

What do each of the following symbols show?

1   **3**   **5**

2   **4**   **6**

A bus driver travels around the ring road (marked yellow). She stops at the hospital which is on her left. Say whether the following places will be on her right or her left as she continues along the ring road route.

1 the football ground   **4** the recreation ground
2 the power station   **5** the retail park
3 the river   **6** the cinema

Where do the following journeys end?

1 Mick leaves the football ground and turns right. He cycles past the police station and turns left on the ring road. After the level crossing he takes the next left and follows the curved road all the way round, taking the left hand fork at the next junction.

2 Alice leaves the cinema and walks along the straight road with the railway on her right. She turns down the second street on her right and cuts through a footpath at the end.

3 Jafar leaves the station and takes the sharp left turn to walk through the school grounds. He cuts through the first footpath at the back of the school, walks straight down the street and turns right. He walks to the end of this road.

4 Leena drives over the bridge across the river and turns left along the ring road. She takes the second turning on her right and follows the curving road until the second turn on her right (this is a sharp turn at the crossroads). She drives to the end of this straight road.

Describe the route taken by a walker starting and ending at the places given below.

1 from the car sales to school
2 from the swimming pool to the burger bar
3 from the cinema to the football ground
4 from the power station to the shops

Now look back at your work in this lesson.
- Can you invent a route for a friend to try?
- Are there any symbols missing from this map?

Module Ⓐ5–Ⓐ8

Practise your skills

Number

Using the times in the box below, write down how long the following activities take.

a few hours	about half an hour	a few minutes	a few seconds

1 Coming to school
2 Brushing your teeth
3 Making a cup of tea
4 Going on holiday to Spain
5 Watching your favourite programme

You have arrived in a station and the time now is shown on the clock.

6 You wanted to catch the 8:35 train. How many minutes are you late?
7 What time will it be after 10 minutes?
8 The next train is at 8:55. How many minutes have you got to wait?
9 Your train journey takes 16 minutes. What time will you arrive?
10 After you arrive you have a five minute walk. What time will you get home?

Handling data

A bakery made three types of doughnuts. This bar chart shows how much the bakery sold today and yesterday.

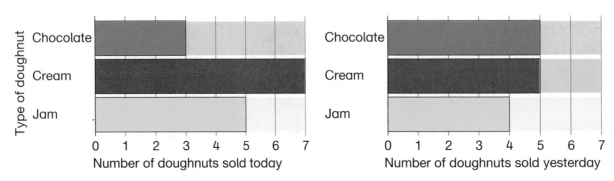

1 Which type of doughnut was the most popular yesterday?
2 Which type of doughnut was the most popular today?

3 Did the bakery sell more or fewer jam doughnuts today than yesterday?
4 Which type was more popular today than yesterday?
5 How many cream doughnuts were sold yesterday? today?

Number

Using the forms of measurement from the box below, choose the best way of measuring these things.

hand span   arm length   pace   your own height

1 The length of a nearest corridor
2 The width of the desk (or table)
3 The height of the classroom
4 The width of a door
5 The length of this textbook

Behind the screen in this picture is exactly the same number of toys you can see in front.

a   b   c

6 How many type **a** toys are there altogether on both sides of the screen?
7 How many type **b** toys are there altogether on both sides of the screen?
8 How many toys are there altogether?

Look at these dials.

9 What speed is the fastest car going?
10 What speed is the slowest car going?

Shape and space

Look at the advertisement signs in this picture.

a

b Sound Maker Music Shop

c

d

e

1. Which sign is the biggest?
2. Which is the smallest?
3. Make a list of the signs which are in-between in order of size, starting with the smallest.

Look at these trees.

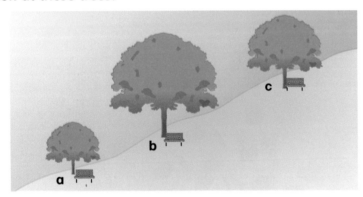

4. Which is the tallest tree?
5. Which is the shortest tree?

Now try this...
You want to change £1.

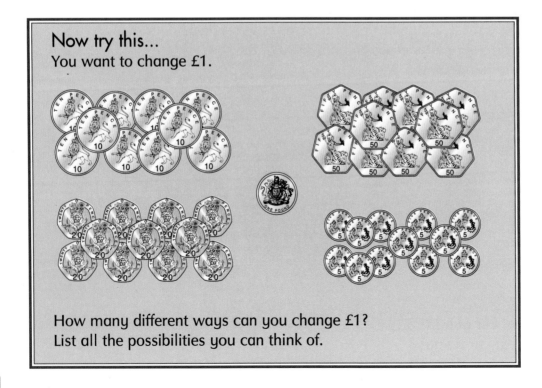

How many different ways can you change £1?
List all the possibilities you can think of.

Check your skills

You can check how well you can do the things listed here. Get your parents and friends to help check them. Your teacher will give you a copy of this page to tick on.

Numbers and measures of time and length

1   I know roughly how many seconds, or minutes, or hours, it takes to do something in daily life. ☐

2   I can find out which of two things takes longer, using my own sense of time. ☐

3   I know how to read digital clocks. ☐

4   I can count things without missing anything and not counting anything twice. ☐

5   I can find a hidden number from the pattern or the sum of the numbers. ☐

6   I can read scales where not all the marks are numbered. ☐

7   I can read, write, and order three-digit numbers like 593. ☐

Shape and space

1   I can find which of two lengths are longer or shorter than others. ☐

2   I can compare the size of things by using measures like a hand span or the height of something. ☐

3   I can fit rectangular shapes together in different ways. ☐

4   I can fit flat shapes other than rectangles. ☐

5   I can understand railway maps and bus maps. ☐

6   I can use street maps. ☐

Sorting and ordering information

1   I can sort things in types and sizes. ☐

2   I can order things and numbers by size or shades of colour. ☐

3   I can make a bar chart for ordered or sorted things. ☐

Acknowledgements

Every effort has been made to contact the holders of copyright material, but if any have been inadvertently overlooked the publishers will be pleased to make the necessary arrangements at the first opportunity.

The publishers would like to thank the following for permission to reproduce photographs (T = Top, B = Bottom, C = Centre, L= Left, R = Right):

The Advertising Archives 30;
Allsport /R Kinnard 46; P Cole 69L; S Forster 77; G Mortimore 102;
© AND Publishers Ltd 1998/ 119;
BBC Photo Library 28;
John Birdsall Photography 17, 23, 25, 53, 69TR;
(Zig IV, 1961 by David Smith), Private Collection/Bridgeman Art Library, London/New York 62;
J Allan Cash Ltd 58;
Express Newspapers 71R;
Leslie Garland Photo Library/A Curtis 92;
Ronald Grant Archive 117;
Robert Harding Picture Library/N Joseph 6, Nakamura 37;
L.W.T. 43;
Andrew Lambert 7, 10, 13, 69CR, 86, 90, 95, 109;
London Aerial Photo Library 121;
London Transport 114;
Metropolitan Police Service 82;
Christine Osborne Pictures 106;
Popperfoto/Reuter 79;
Rex Features Ltd 20, 84, 94;
The Stock Market 73, 75CL,CR&L;
Tony Stone Images 33, 50, 56, 74, 75R;
Tesco Photographic Unit 88;
C & S Thompson 22, 71L.